SO-AXA-733

ZOO

Same planet. Different world.

Foreword

In the 1960s a group of citizens had the foresight to campaign for a new zoo for Toronto, to replace the smaller, more traditional Riverdale Zoo. Concepts of zoos were changing and

Torontonians wanted a modern zoo that would reflect Toronto's status as a world class city. The planning team envisioned a zoo with a diverse collection of plants and animals, grouped according to their native continents, and exhibits with open viewing and a minimum of barriers. A beautiful site was selected adjacent to the Rouge River, enveloping a land expanse rich in natural and cultural features. The Metro Toronto Zoo, as it was known then, opened on August 15, 1974.

From these early beginnings, the Toronto Zoo continues to evolve as one of Canada's best-loved attractions and a wonderful family experience. As one of the largest zoos in North America, with approximately 500 species and 5,000 specimens, the Toronto Zoo has a professional staff of animal keepers, horticulturists, veterinarians, curators, educators and others who are highly committed to the conservation of endangered species and spaces.

Today our focus extends well beyond our public face to include leadership in protecting biodiversity and contributing to a global conservation effort. In 1974, our planet lost one species per year. Today the global extinction rate has soared to three species each day. This critical loss of biodiversity has propelled the Toronto Zoo to become a "Modern Ark", saving rare species and creating a living classroom for lessons that will help sustain our planet.

Situated in the heart of the Rouge Park, Canada's first national urban park, the Toronto Zoo is well-positioned to serve as the gateway for the new federal park. The potential for enhanced collaborative opportunities in the areas of education, conservation and guest experiences, will shape the Toronto Zoo of the future.

The animals at Toronto Zoo are ambassadors for their counterparts in the wild, helping to convey the importance of wildlife conservation and habitat preservation. This book is a tribute to all the plants and animals in our care. I sincerely hope it brings appreciation and insight into the importance of biodiversity and the role that people must play if animals and their habitats are to endure.

John Tracogna
Chief Executive Officer
Toronto Zo

🐾 toronto **ZOO**

Copyright © 2013 Board of Management Toronto Zoo

Designed and Printed by
SOUVENIRS™
THE POSTCARD FACTORY.
A Division of The Weisdorf Group of Companies Inc.
Tel: 1-800-563-7678

Managing Editor and Text
Michelle Egan

Art Direction and Design
Mary Imamura Power

Editors
Kelly Bentley, Heather House

Principal Photography
Ken Ardill

Also, special thanks to: Dyann Powley, Kathryn Connolly, Elaine Christens, Maria Franke, Bob Johnson, Cindy Lee, Tom Mason, William Rapley, Andre Wattie.

Other photography credits

Photographer	Description	Page
Dominque Berteaux	Arctic Fox	68
John Brunjes	Snow Goose	70
Michelle Egan	Gum Tree	117
Marg Fleming	*Clerodendrum speciosissimum* (Java Glory-bower)	33
	Ficus religiosa (Bo Tree)	34
	Platycerium bifurcatum (Staghorn Fern)	34
	Asplenium nidus (Bird's-Nest Fern)	35
	Acanthus montanus (Mountain Thistle)	60
	Kigelia africana (Sausage Tree)	61
	Calliandra haematopcephala (Powderpuff)	95
	Bromeliaceae	95
	Heliconia rostrata (Lobster Claw)	95
	Neomarica gracilis (Walking Iris)	95
	Bamboo	117
Jellybean Imaging Inc.	Kids Zoo photos	11

All rights reserved.
No part of this book may be used or reproduced in any manner whatsoever without the written permission of the Board of Management Toronto Zoo.

100%
Paper from well-managed forests
FSC
www.fsc.org FSC™ C023083

Printed in Korea.
Printed with vegetable based inks.

Ref: SGB-TZ 003-E (Fourth Edition)

INDO-MALAYA

AFRICA

CANADA

TUNDRA

AMERICAS

AUSTRALASIA

EURASIA

toronto ZOO
Same planet. Different world.

Table of Contents

WELCOME TO
TORONTO ZOO

Opened in 1974, the Toronto Zoo was founded for the purpose of exhibiting and conserving a diversity of species within the animal and plant kingdoms.

TORONTO ZOO VISION

Toronto Zoo will be a dynamic and exciting action centre that inspires people to love, respect and protect wildlife and wild spaces.

The Zoo is 287 hectares and is divided into zoogeographic regions. There are four major tropical indoor pavilions and several smaller indoor viewing areas, plus numerous outdoor exhibits. In total, there are 10 kilometres of walking trails to explore. Currently over 5,000 animals representing just over 450 species make the Toronto Zoo their home. The annual cost of feeding our animals is approximately $1.2 million. Not to be excluded, the Zoo's plant collection is valued at $5 million!

The Toronto Zoo is a not for profit facility, funded by the City of Toronto, Zoo members, Zoo donors, and Zoo visitors.

FIVE FABULOUS WAYS TO HELP WILDLIFE

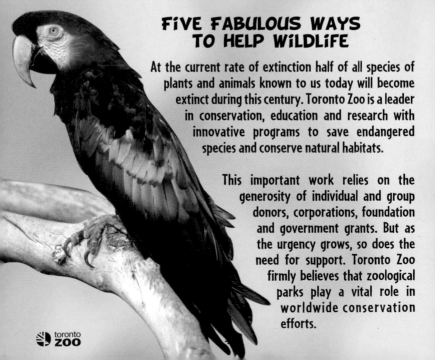

At the current rate of extinction half of all species of plants and animals known to us today will become extinct during this century. Toronto Zoo is a leader in conservation, education and research with innovative programs to save endangered species and conserve natural habitats.

This important work relies on the generosity of individual and group donors, corporations, foundation and government grants. But as the urgency grows, so does the need for support. Toronto Zoo firmly believes that zoological parks play a vital role in worldwide conservation efforts.

toronto ZOO

PHOTOGRAPHY AT THE ZOO

Virtually all of the photographs in this book were taken by Ken Ardill, a Toronto Zoo volunteer. His photographs are beautiful, colourful and have such great character. Here are a few tips from Ken for taking pictures at the Zoo.

Almost any type of equipment from a simple "point and shoot" to an advanced digital single lens reflex can be used to produce great pictures. Naturally, with more advanced equipment you can deal with a wider range of subjects, however, by gearing subject choices to the capabilities of your equipment, some truly exceptional pictures can be taken.

When photographing animals with wire screening around the enclosures use your camera's widest aperture to reduce depth of field and throw the wire out of focus. Also, try to get your lens as close to the wire as possible (without crossing any barriers). Try to avoid areas where the wire is in strong sunlight. Reflections from the wire may show up as flare in your picture. The same technique can be used to successfully photograph through the glass front of the enclosures in the pavilions. By placing the lens right against the glass, the reflections and flare will be minimized when using an electronic flash.

Here's how to help...

1. Create habitat in your own backyard: Building a toad abode, planting pollinator-friendly plants, or setting up a bird feeder are just a few of the ways your can support your local wildlife.

2. Learn more about the Zoo and the easy steps you can take to conserve wildlife by taking part in one of the Zoo's many educational offerings for children, adults, families, or students.

3. Become a thoughtful consumer, make purchasing decisions based on guides such as the Seafood Watch card.

4. Support the Zoo's conservation and research programs by adopting an animal, donating money to the Endangered Species Reserve Fund, or supporting one of our fundraising campaigns.

5. Connect to nature by visiting a local park or participating in local conservation events such as shoreline cleanups.

For information on supporting the Toronto Zoo please contact Toronto Zoo Development at 416-392-9114 or visit torontozoo.com/Support The Zoo

toronto ZOO

GREEN SIGHTINGS ON-SITE

Green Vision Statement

The Toronto Zoo has a strong record of environmental protection and of energy efficient operation management. The Zoo stimulates staff, volunteers and the public to live sustainably in balance with Nature. We understand and accept that climate change is a real threat to the earth's biodiversity, perhaps most acutely to our own species. We accept that humans are largely responsible for global warming as a result of our use of non-renewable energy resources and the emission of greenhouse gases. We encourage people to lessen their ecological footprint on the earth.

GREEN ROOFS

Green roofs, also known as 'living roofs' or 'eco-roofs', are the wave of the future in sustainable design. Toronto Zoo has set up a green roof system on top of the Australasia Pavilion, and African penguin and polar bear exhibits. Green roofs cool and clean the air around them, provide refuge for birds and insects, help combat climate change, and retain rainwater.

GEOEXCHANGE TECHNOLOGY IN ACTION! LION-TAILED MACAQUE EXHIBIT

In June 2008 the Toronto Zoo opened its first geothermal exhibit, at the lion-tailed macaques (Indomalaya Outdoor Exhibits). This exhibit, previously heated in the off-season by overhead electric radiant heaters, is now warmed from below by efficient and renewable geothermal energy from the earth's core – and cooled in the summer the same way. Visitors can have a hands-on experience with this innovative technology by feeling the mulch temperature in the sample area just outside of the exhibit.

Geothermal systems have the least environmental impacts of any space heating technology today.

Geothermal energy in action - notice the snow free exhibit floor

ICE BEAR SYSTEM

The latest green technology is the Ice Bear storage system which can be seen just outside the Caribou Café. The Ice Bear unit uses off-peak electricity in the middle of the night to make a big block of ice. The ice then slowly melts throughout the next day. This energy is used during the day in the building's air conditioning system to cool the air!

SOLAR THERMAL PANELS ADMINISTRATION SUPPORT CENTRE

The roof of the Zoo's administration complex has been equipped with 50 solar thermal panels. The system transfers the energy from the sun to the hot water supply for the building – reducing carbon dioxide by 40 tonnes per year and natural gas use by 50%.

BACKYARD CONSERVATION

Conservation begins in our own backyard. Toronto Zoo removes invasive species and preserves important urban habitats to protect rare species and to keep common species common.

For more information on these and other Green Initiatives at the Toronto Zoo, check out torontozoo.com/conservation/green.asp

toronto ZOO

PHONEAPES ™ PROGRAM

In March 2010, the Toronto Zoo launched "Phone Apes" their very own cell phone recycling program.

The purpose of this program is to raise awareness about the negative effects of cell phone manufacturing on wildlife habitat. Inside all cell phones is a mineral called coltan. Coltan has become one of the world's most sought-after minerals because it is used to create tantalum, a key ingredient in electronic circuitry. About 80% of the world's coltan is mined in central Africa and these mining activities are disrupting lowland gorilla and numerous other species' habitat. By recycling your cell phone, you are helping to decrease the demand for coltan. For every cell phone collected, the Zoo receives $0.70. All proceeds support the conservation of great apes in the wild.

Phone Apes™
recycling
cell phones for
conservation

phoneapes.com

Adopt-A-Pond Program
(torontozoo.com/AdoptAPond/):

The Adopt-A-Pond Wetland Conservation Program provides educators, students and community groups with stewardship resources and educational opportunities to protect, restore and conserve wetland habitats and biodiversity. While the program runs a number of projects on site at Toronto Zoo to protect and celebrate wetland biodiversity, Adopt-A-Pond also has six major off-site initiatives that address wetland conservation issues in Ontario, including:

- Ontario Turtle Tally
- Frogwatch Ontario
- Wetland Guardians
- Urban Turtle Initiative
- Healthy Water, Healthy Wildlife
- Turtle Island Conservation

Contact the Adopt-A-Pond Coordinator at aap@torontozoo.ca for more information.

Great Lakes Conservation
(torontozoo.com/conservation/GreatLakesConservation.asp):

Toronto Zoos' Great Lakes Outreach Program is a FREE, curriculum-based education program that encourages students, educators and families to "Keep our Great Lakes Great" while learning about five local fish species at risk. Beyond the classroom, the Great Lakes Program also contributes to habitat rehabilitation though community events and tree planting.

Aqua-links:

A sister program to the Great Lakes Conservation initiative, Aqua-Links is an exciting new conservation effort at the Zoo linking students in Ontario with students in Uganda. Focusing on these two Great Lakes regions of the world, the program fosters stewardship and appreciation for water as a precious resource, as well as, for the fish that call these lakes home.

ECOExecutives
(torontozoo.com/conservation/ecoexecutives.asp) :

The ECOexecutives program offers high impact lessons in sustainability for businesses. Through exclusive behind the scenes tours and interactive content sessions participants see the link between sustainable business choices and biodiversity protection. A fantastic opportunity to meet other business professionals with the same goals in mind...and touch a rhino!

toronto ZOO

DISCOVERY ZONE

Explore the Discovery Zone, featuring the Kids Zoo, a dynamic, interactive children's wildlife experience, Splash Island, an exciting two-acre water play area where visitors explore our local watershed, and the Waterside Theatre, home of exciting family entertainment.

MEET A BARN OWL!

The shape of a barn owl's face is key to helping this nocturnal flyer find its prey in the dark. The very prominent "facial disc" works like a radar dish, channeling the sounds made by voles, mice, shrews, and other tasty tidbits to the owl's ears.

GET UP CLOSE AND PERSONAL WITH AN ALPACA!

Related to llamas and camels, the alpaca has a long neck which enables it to see long distances, so it can spot a predator (mountain lion, coyote, bear, or other carnivore) and escape to safety. A special high-pitched braying sound warns the herd that danger lurks nearby. Alpacas are domesticated animals bred for thousands of years for their soft coat used in textiles.

SEE A STRIPED SKUNK!

The skunk is known for its infamous spray, or musk, and is able to produce a fine cloud of mist, or to direct a concentrated stream of stinky spray on animals up to 4.8 metres away. That's like standing at the muskrat lodge in the Kids Zoo and hitting a target at the turtle shells! Skunks are important wild neighbours because they eat insects and rodents, controlling the populations of these animals.

toronto ZOO

toronto ZOO

CONSERVATION AT TORONTO ZOO

At the Toronto Zoo, our goal is not just to preserve the animals within our care but also to ensure the future of animals in the wild. To that end, we remain profoundly committed to international con-servation efforts. We currently participate in 100 Species Survival Plans (SSPs) for animals ranging from polar bears to Komodo dragons.

Initiated by the Association of Zoos and Aquariums (AZA), SSPs are North American collective strategies for the conservation of endangered species. An SSP may begin with field research to preserve habitats, and from there may lead to maintaining the population in captivity by implementing a breeding program. Ideally, if protected habitat remains, the offspring will be released back to the wild.

Along with participation in the SSP program, the Toronto Zoo, often in conjunction with other organizations, takes part in many important projects. These include 22 local and international conservation projects and 46 ongoing research projects such as breeding strategies, nutrition, and behaviour.

As of 2013, Toronto Zoo SSPs include:

- 51 mammals
- 31 birds
- 12 reptiles
- 2 amphibians
- 4 fish

NOT EVALUATED	DATA DEFICIENT	LEAST CONCERN	NEAR THREATENED	VULNERABLE	‹ ENDANGERED ›	CRITICALLY ENDANGERED	EXTINCT IN THE WILD	EXTINCT
			NT	VU	EN	CR	EW	EX

This international scale is used to classify the degree of risk to any individual species. Look for it on site.

RETURN OF THE GIANT PANDAS!

The Toronto Zoo is excited, and proud, to welcome Da Mao (male) and Er Shun (female) a breeding giant panda pair from China. The last time giant pandas were at the Toronto Zoo was in 1985 when they came for a three-month stay in the summer months. This time the giant pandas will spend a minimum of five years in Toronto, followed by five years in Calgary. Da Mao and Er Shun were chosen to come to Canada because they are a good genetic match for breeding.

This exciting conservation loan, which re-confirms our long-term conservation partnership agreement between China and Canada, began many years ago but was finalized on February 11, 2012 in Chongqing, China. Canadian Prime Minister Stephen Harper witnessed Toronto Zoo CEO John Tracogna and Calgary Zoo President and CEO Clement Lanthier, along with Mme Hu, VP, Secretary-General of the Chinese Association of Zoological Gardens, sign the official Giant Panda Cooperation Agreement confirming the arrival of Da Mao and Er Shun and making this important conservation partnership official.

Today, the North American zoos that have pandas include: the Smithsonian's National Zoo (Washington, DC), San Diego Zoo (California), Zoo Atlanta (Georgia), Memphis Zoo (Tennessee), and Chapultepec Zoo (Mexico City).

MEET OUR GIANT PANDAS

Our female giant panda, Er Shun (meaning double smoothness) was born on August 10, 2007 at Chongqing Zoological Garden. She was raised by her mother, Yalaoer; her father's name was Lingling. Chongqing is the largest city in Southwestern China, is Toronto's sister city and has a population of 28.8 million.

Our male giant panda, Da Mao was born on September 1, 2008 at Chengdu Research Base (the most successful panda breedng facility in China). He was the first cub of his mother, Mao Mao, and his name follows the Chinese tradition of recognizing this relationship.

toronto ZOO

GIANT PANDA
Ailuropoda melanoleuca

Comparison of genetics, behavior and reproduction have confirmed that indeed bears are the giant pandas' closest relative. Wild giant pandas are only located in central China, specifically within the provinces of Sichuan, Gansu, and Shanxi. They once lived in lowland areas, but farming, forest clearing, and other development now restrict giant pandas to a few isolated areas of dense bamboo undergrowth in the mountain forests.

A giant panda's diet is 99% bamboo and they are very selective in the types of bamboo they will eat. The other 1% of their diet consists of other grasses and small rodents or musk deer fawns.

Pandas are a highly specialized animal with unique adaptations. An extra, opposable digit (thumb) on the front paw is actually a modified sesamoid (wrist) bone that enables the panda to dexterously grasp bamboo stalks. Strong jaw muscles along with very wide, flat molar and premolar teeth enable them to crush the tough, fibrous bamboo. Their stomach walls are extremely muscular to help digest the woody diet and the gut is covered with a thick layer of mucus to protect against splinters.

Because the giant panda digestive system is more similar to that of a carnivore they have only a few of the enzymes necessary to digest the cellulose contained in the bamboo. Thus, most of the bamboo passes through their digestive tract undigested, causing giant pandas to relieve themselves dozens of times a day! To make up for their inefficient digestion, they need to consume a comparatively large amount of food in order to extract enough nutrients.

The average giant panda eats 9 to 14 kg of bamboo each day. In order to obtain this much food a panda must spend 10 to 16 hours a day foraging and eating. The rest of the time is spent mostly sleeping and resting.

When they are born, panda cubs are about the size of a cell phone, weighing 85 to 140 grams (lighter than an apple)! They are blind, helpless, and covered with a thin layer of fur. Female giant pandas are only receptive to breeding once a year for a period of 24 to 72 hours.

The Chinese refer to giant pandas as "Big Bear Cats" since their eyes have vertical slits like a cat's, not round pupils like a bear's.

CONSERVATION OF GIANT PANDAS

In China, the giant panda is a national treasure. It has been the World Wildlife Fund's (WWF's) logo since 1961. The inspiration for this logo came from Chi-Chi, a giant panda that had arrived at the London Zoo in 1961, the same year WWF was formed. The giant panda is one of the most beloved animals in the world and is perhaps the most powerful symbol in the world for wildlife conservation. It is also one of the most endangered species in the world, with only around 1,600 left in the wild.

One of the main reasons that pandas have become endangered is habitat destruction. As the population in China continues to grow, panda habitat gets taken over by development, pushing them into smaller and less liveable areas. Habitat destruction also leads to food shortages. Pandas feed on several varieties of bamboo at different times of the year. If one type of bamboo is destroyed by development, it can leave the panda with nothing to eat during that time, increasing the risk of starvation. Besides habitat loss, a further threat is the periodic, large-scale die-off of bamboo at intervals of 15 to 120 years. Poaching of pandas, was a serious problem in the past, but is no longer considered a threat since the Chinese government has adopted conservation initiatives for this species.

Today, there are 63 panda reserves in China that are attempting to preserve panda habitat and to support breeding programs. Logging has been banned in these reserves and reforestation programs are being implemented to reclaim agricultural area. Corridors are being created to connect fragmented habitat. As well as in Asia, many zoos in Australia, Europe and North America are involved in protecting the giant panda from possible extinction. Captive breeding success with giant pandas has increased dramatically in the last 20 years due to technology and reproduction methodology advancements

and the hard work of international zoos and research facilities working with panda scientists and reserves in China. There will be over 350 giant pandas in captivity when the 2012 breeding season is completed. A new target of 500 individuals has been set to support reintroduction studies which are returning pandas to the wild. This research is currently underway and is very promising for giant panda conservation efforts.

GiANT PANDAS NEED YOUR HELP!
HERE'S WHAT YOU CAN DO:

Share...
what you have learned today by becoming a fan of the Toronto Zoo facebook page.

How this helps pandas:
The more people know about the threats to pandas and what is being done to help them, the more support the animals will get.

Donate...
by adding coins to the panda sculpture at the giant panda exhibit, by adopting a panda*, or by contributing to panda conservation through Toronto Zoo's Endangered Species Reserve Fund* or Pandas International.

* information available from the Membership Office or torontozoo. com

How this helps pandas:
It is expensive to care for, conduct research and breed pandas, and to protect their habitat–the money you contribute will help to fund these activities.

Act...
to limit your contribution to climate change by conserving electricity and reducing carbon emissions from transportation-related pollution.

How this helps pandas:
Animals that live on mountains are particularly affected by climate change, as increasing temperatures cause their habitats to shrink.

> The Toronto Zoo supports a bamboo and habitat restoration project in China through the Endangered Species Reserve Fund in collaboration with the Memphis Zoo. In addition, the Toronto Zoo employs a Reproductive Physiologist who investigates ways to improve the reproduction of endangered species, and will be applying her expertise to our very own breeding program for Da Mao and Er Shun.

toronto ZOO

Indo-Malaya

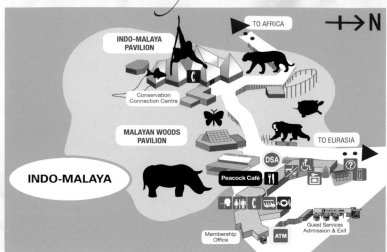

Southeast Asia consists of countries and archipelagos spanning the Pacific and Indian oceans. Dense jungles, extensive coastlines, mountains, and large river systems produce thousands of flowering plants and tree species. It's hot all year round, with distinct rainy and dry seasons, in this beautiful region of diverse flora and fauna. Explore the Malayan Woods Pavilion where you walk among colourful butterflies and watch them feed on fruit slices placed among the foliage. Outside, visit the greater one-horned rhinos, Malayan tapir, and lion-tailed macaques. Inside the Indo-Malaya Pavilion, you'll find multi-level viewing of the orangutans, a large semicircular aquarium that will surround you with freshwater fishes, giant snakes, tropical birds flying above, and an up-close look at rare Sumatran tigers.

Greater One Horned Rhinoceros
Rhinoceros unicornis

Like their African relative, the greater one horned rhino is also characterized by poor eyesight, but has a good sense of hearing and smell. Unlike the white rhino from Africa, these rhinos have only one horn. The Indian rhino's upper lip is prehensile (has the ability to grasp), and is used to feed on grasses, fruits, leaves, trees, and shrubs. Rhinos are often found wallowing in the mud to protect their skin from sunburn (much like the hippopotamus), and the mud coating also protects them from biting insects and parasites. Indian rhinos are solitary animals and generally try to escape from an enemy, rather than attack. Most of the day is spent resting in the shade or mud, with activity and feeding time taking place at night and in the early morning.

Malayan Tapir
Tapirus indicus

You may think this animal is related to the anteater; however, it is actually a cousin of horses and rhinos! The Malayan tapir is a peculiar-looking animal with distinctive black and white colouring that provides good camouflage in the shadowy moonlight of tropical rainforests. Malayan tapirs live in southeast Asia in the undergrowth of rainforests, spending most of their day bedded down in dense underbrush. Their trunk-like snout is used as a foraging tool and sensor. Because their eyesight is so poor, they rely on their nose to find vegetation to eat. Tactile hairs on the tip of the snout act as sensors by touching the ground. When suitable food is found, they lift their nose out of the way and clip off the vegetation with their incisors.

A baby tapir has different colouring than adults. It is black with white stripes and spots, looking something like a black and white watermelon on legs!

toronto ZOO

Lion-tailed Macaque
Macaca silenus

The lion-tailed macaque is one of the smallest of the 15 species of macaques. Found in southern India in evergreen forests, lion-tailed macaques are endangered because their habitat is being cleared to grow coffee, tea, and eucalyptus. Lion-tailed macaques are omnivores, eating mostly fruits, leaves, flowers, insects, and small birds or mammals. They have specialized cheek pouches in which they store food while feeding. They climb and jump around easily in the trees; they also sleep and rest in the trees, wedged in between branches. Along with a tail resembling a lion's, they also have a grey mane around their face similar to a lion's mane. The rest of their body is covered in a glossy black coat, which helps keep them hidden in the shady areas of the forest.

Turn to pages 6 and 7 to learn about how the zoo uses geothermal heating in the macaque exhibit.

Jumbo Gourami
Osphronemus goramy

Jumbo gouramies are large herbivorous fish, found in southeast Asia and have several interesting features. They are bubble or froth nesters, which means the male builds a nest by taking air bubbles in his mouth where they are coated with mucus to help them stick together. The bubbles are then blown out to create a bubble nest at the surface of the water. The male places the eggs in the nest and guards them until they hatch. Gouramies have also adapted to living in stagnant waters with low oxygen levels by breathing air directly.

Black-breasted Leaf Turtle
Geoemyda spengleri spengleri

These small turtles inhabit the mountainous regions of southern China and northern Vietnam. They prefer humid places near streams, and mountain forests. Their food, snails, worms, small insects, and crustaceans is found in and around the streams. Black-breasted turtles are mostly terrestrial, entering the water usually just to drink and soak. This turtle actually looks like a fallen leaf, which helps it to stay hidden among leaves in the forest. The black-breasted leaf turtle is severely endangered. Their populations are declining because of their popularity in the Asian food market and pet trade.

Sulawesi Babirusa
Babyrousa celebensis

Pronunciation: soo-lah-wey-see bab-uh-roo-suh. The name babirusa originates from the Malay words babi "pig" and rusa "deer" as the tusks resemble antlers. Sulawesi babirusa are found only on the Indonesian island of Sulawesi. Babirusas are part of the pig family, and are one of the oldest living members of this family. The most impressive feature of the babirusa are the male's canines (or tusks), which grow upward through the top of the snout, penetrating the skull, and curve back towards the head instead of growing into the mouth. They can be as long as 30 cm or more. These long curved tusks may be used by the males to protect their faces and eyes when challenging each other for the rights to females. The longer the tusks, the more attractive a male is to a female, and thus they serve as a symbol of rank and fitness. The females have only the lower tusks in most cases, but they may also have small upper tusks. Babirusas live primarily in tropical forests and along the shores of rivers and lakes. They are omnivores, eating mostly fruit, leaves or grasses, but will also eat mushrooms, nuts, insect larvae and sometimes small animals.

Clouded Leopard
Panthera nebulosa

Although they are smaller than other leopard species, these cats are still very powerful. They have strong jaws, long canines, and a sturdy build that allows them to kill fairly large prey, such as deer and boars. Clouded leopards spend most of their time in the trees. They are able to move acrobatically through the trees, hunting from above. When they spot their prey, the leopard springs directly onto it from overhanging branches. They have very flexible ankle joints that enable them to run down a tree headfirst, a unique characteristic among cats. Clouded leopards are mostly solitary, except during mating season. Their name comes from their cloud-like spots.

Butterfly

Butterflies feed on nectar, fruit juice and sap for energy and are strictly liquid feeders as adults. They are important pollinators for specific plants and can transport pollen over great distances.

toronto ZOO

TURTLES iN TROUBLE
SOUTHEAST ASIAN TURTLES

Asia has the richest diversity of turtles and tortoises on earth. Turtles have been an important part of Asian culture for thousands of years. Many people place tremendous significance on the value of turtles for medicinal and health-giving properties. As southeast Asia's population and economic well-being increases, consumer demand is decimating wild turtle populations. Today, almost ¾ of Asia's 90 species of turtles are considered endangered or threatened. Toronto Zoo is helping by providing funding for wildlife rescue centres and support for wildlife control officers to enforce regulations for the illegal trade.

Vietnamese Box Turtle
Cistoclemmys galbinifrons

The Vietnamese box turtle has a unique shell in that it has a hinge on the bottom shell (plastron). This hinge allows the turtle to tightly close the front and back portions of the shell when the limbs are retracted. This provides very effective protection against predators. They can be found living in rainforests, marshes and rice paddies. They feed on berries, leaves, grass, worms, slugs, crickets, small frogs, and occasionally small snakes. Females lay their eggs in a nest of leaves and twigs, which they create themselves, and cover them. They will stay with the nest to protect it for a few days.

 To help forest dwelling species, we encourage visitors to purchase sustainably harvested wood products with the Forest Stewardship Council (FSC) logo.

Burmese Star Tortoise
Geochelone platynota

Found in dry forests of central Myanmar (Burma). These turtles are active during the day, spending their time searching for food on the forest floor and seeking shade under vegetation during the hottest parts of the day. When these tortoises are in the grass, the yellow stripes on the tortoise's shell helps to protect them from predators by breaking the shape of the tortoise and disguising them. The Burmese star tortoise feeds on grasses, mushrooms and fruit, but may also eat insects and larvae. This species is considered virtually extinct in the wild, but a few individuals continue to show up in the markets.

Malaysian Painted Turtle
Callagur borneoensis

Found in southern Thailand and farther south into Malaysia, Sumatra, and Borneo, these turtles are in trouble. Malaysian painted turtles are endangered because of pollution in the streams they inhabit, as well as, being overcollected for food and the pet trade. Their colour varies from light brown to olive, yellow, and cream. Amazingly, during the mating season, the male's head becomes white and a red stripe develops between his eyes —the name "painted" turtle comes from this mating colour. When the female is nesting, she digs a deep hole (30 cm) on a beach, lays her eggs, covers the hole, and returns to the water. Malaysian painted turtles are vegetarians and live mainly in the estuaries of medium to large rivers.

toronto **ZOO**

Tentacled Snake
Erpeton tentaculatum

Tentacled snakes are small (50–75 cm long) snakes found in coastal southeast Asia, including Vietnam, Thailand, and Cambodia. During the dry season, they may bury themselves under mud until the rains return. Tentacled snakes spend all their time in the water and are helpless on land. They live in slow-moving fresh water in shallow streams, ditches, and rice paddies. As their name suggests, they have two tentacles at the side of their snout. The tentacles don't appear to serve a specific function, but may help in detecting moving prey in murky water. Tentacled snakes feed exclusively on small fish. Other specializations of the tentacled snake include rear fangs, which are mildly venomous, and nostrils that can be closed underwater. They can remain underwater for long periods before needing to return to the surface for air. Females bear live young, approximately 5-13 per litter.

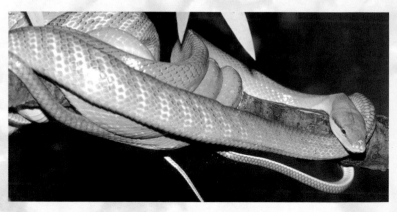

Red-tailed Green Ratsnake
Gonyosoma oxycephala

The red-tailed green ratsnake is slender and smooth-scaled with a red tail and vivid blue tongue. Its luminous green body and yellowish underside helps it to stay camouflaged in the lush swamp and forest areas it inhabits. The green on their back blends in with the foliage while the yellow tones in the skin match the leaf-filtered light. For added protection, they have evolved to look and behave like a venomous pit viper that occupies the same habitat. This adaptation is called "mimicry," which is an anti-predatory device found in nature. Their diet consists of eggs, birds, frogs, lizards, and small mammals, including rats.

Sumatran Orangutan
Pongo pygmaeus abelii

It's hard to resist these playful primates. Unfortunately, they are a critically endangered species from the Island of Sumatra where their habitat is being destroyed for agricultural use. They spend most of their time high in the trees of tropical rainforests. Orangutans' long arms and long, hooked hands allow them to use a "hook grip" to swing from tree to tree. Their feet are just as useful; the big toe is opposable and thus acts the same as the thumb on a human hand. Usually orangutans prefer to eat fruit, but they will also feed on leaves, nuts, insects, and young birds or small mammals. They are able to find these foods high in the trees; therefore, they generally don't need to go down to the ground. They drink water from rainfall catches in the forest leaves. Orangutans will spread out in a forest and live in small family groups made up of a mother with one or two youngsters. Nearly all males live solitary lives except when mating.

Orangutans are covered in reddish-brown shaggy hair except for the face, ears, and throat, which are bare. Mature males are characterized by large cheek flanges, protruding at the side of the head, and pronounced throat pouches. Like humans, they have a set of 32 teeth including 2 large canine teeth. At birth a young orangutan weighs only 1.6–1.9 kg; however, they will grow to be 50–90 kg (males) or 30–50 kg (females).

The biggest threat to orangutans is non-sustainable palm oil farming. Palm oil is found in many foods and bath products; in fact, you likely eat and use palm oil every day. Palm oil plantations are not part of the rainforest, the home of orangutans and many other animals, but are an introduced crop. In order to grow these plantations, much of the rainforest is being cut down, followed by uncontrolled burning to clear the land. Due to the large amount of deforestation and habitat loss involved, it is estimated that orangutans will be extinct in the wild in 10-15 years if the palm oil industry, deforestation, and burning of peat forest do not subside.

Want to make sustainable purchasing decisions?
Please visit: cmzoo.org/Conservation/PalmOilCrisis

toronto ZOO

INDO-MALAYA AQUARiUM

This large aquarium (53,000 L) has over a dozen species of freshwater fishes found in the Indo-Malayan region. Each species in the tank has its own unique characteristics. The fish range in size from 5 cm to 35 cm long. Many of the fish, but especially the **clown barbs** *(Puntius everetti)*, swim together in groups called "schools" or shoals. This behaviour provides protection in numbers — they may confuse predators by appearing larger. The **spanner barbs** *(Puntius lageristriga)* are one of the bigger species of schooling fish in the tank. The **tinfoil barbs** *(Barbodes schwanenfeldi)* are the largest species in the tank. They also have a fairly long life expectancy; some of our tinfoil barbs have lived over 25 years. Unlike other fish species, males and females are different colours in some barb species. The **rosy barbs** *(Puntius conchonius)* demonstrate an interesting characteristic: they exhibit courting behaviour that consists of a male and female swimming in tight circles for about 10 seconds. The males are black with a red nose and the females and juvenile males and females are striped red and black. Also in the tank is the **red-tailed shark** *(Epalzeorhynchos bicolor)*, an algae scraper (not a member of the shark family); they can be seen swimming up and down the walls of the tank. Forest degradation is affecting the streams and waterways these fish inhabit.

Gaur
Bos gaurus

This species of wild cattle lives in tropical grasslands and forests in India, Myanmar, and on the Malay Peninsula. In the dry season, gaurs live in moist forest valleys and move to higher and drier elevations during the rainy season. Gaurs are extremely large animals, as tall as 2 m and weighing 1,000 kg or more. They generally live in herds of 5–6, sometimes up to 20 or more. Younger ones may leave the herd to form a bachelor group, and old bulls often live alone. The gaur feeds on grasses and young bamboo shoots. When attack is necessary, a gaur approaches its opponent broadside, lowering its head and hindquarters and striking from the side with its horns. It is the only wild ox that does not attack frontally with its horns. In India, domestic cattle graze in the same forest habitat as gaur, exposing them to diseases normally only found in domestic livestock, such as hoof-and-mouth disease. This and loss of habitat are the main factors leading to their diminished population size.

toronto **ZOO**

Malayan Bonytongue
Scleropages formosus

Malayan bonytongues live in weedy, slow-moving streams, canals, and swamps. Growing up to 90 cm in length and weighing as much as 7.2 kg, they are one of the most beautiful freshwater fishes because of their colouring. As mouth brooders, the male carries the female's eggs in his throat where they are incubated for seven days. During this time he does not eat. The eggs are fairly large and are few in number. Malayan bonytongues are a predatory species, feeding on insects when they are young, and other fish, small aquatic birds, and amphibians when they are adults. Found in Asia, they are now endangered due to habitat loss and overfishing for food.

Reticulated Python
Python reticulatus

Considered the longest snake in the world, the reticulated python has been measured at 9.8 m long (average size is 4–6 m). They are named "reticulated" (meaning a netlike pattern) because of the complex geometric pattern on their skin. Reticulated pythons are strictly carnivorous, feeding mostly on birds and mammals. With its large body and muscles, the snake constricts its prey before eating. Its versatile jaw enables it to swallow food headfirst and whole, even though the prey is often larger in diameter than the snake's body. Swallowing such large prey is possible because the connection of its lower jaw to the skull is very loose and works like a double-jointed hinge. Thus, the snake can drop its lower jaw at the back, while the front of its lower jaw expands sideways as only a ligament connects the bottom halves (there is no bony "chin"). Its sharp teeth hold the prey in place while the mobile jaws "walk" up and over the animal.

Mekong Barb
Catlocarpio siamensis

The Mekong barb is found in the Cambodian Mekong River system. It is the National fish of the Kingdom of Cambodia. This fish is found in deep pools along the edges of large rivers. They feed on phytoplankton, algae, seaweed and fruits of submerged terrestrial plants. They are threatened by overfishing, river traffic, dams, habitat loss and pollution. The Mekong barb is a tetraploid species, which means they have four of each chromosome unlike most animals that are diploid and have two of each chromosome.

Sun catfish (Sun Cats)
Horabagrus brachysoma

The sun catfish is a large catfish that is known for its distinct black spot right behind the gill plate. It is found in slow moving streams and rivers of the Western Ghats of Kerala, India. It feeds on smaller fish, crustaceans, molluscs and plant matter. Adults may also eat terrestrial insects and even frogs. Sun catfish are an important food fish in India and are also sold in the aquarium trade. The sun catfish is considered to be an endangered species. Overexploitation, habitat alteration, pollution and related environmental impacts on their natural habitat have considerably reduced populations of this species by 60–70% during the last few years.

Fish Rescue: Toronto Zoo is working with several partners to inform citizens to never release unwanted aquarium fishes, turtles or plants. They can, and do, survive causing problems for our native species. The Fish Rescue program hopes to avoid problems with introduced species outcompeting or preying on native flora and fauna.

toronto ZOO

White-handed Gibbon
Hylobates lar

Born almost completely white, only their hands, feet, and part of the face will be white after the age of 2–4 years. The rest of their body ranges in colour from black to cream. This colour variation is not sex-related. White-handed gibbons are found in the tropical forests of southeast Asia (southern Burma, Thailand and Cambodia, Malaya and Sumatra). The gibbon's arms are twice the length of its body and about one and a half times the length of its legs. White-handed gibbons fly through the trees, jumping and swinging, covering 9 m or more in a single movement; this helps them to escape rapidly from danger.

Spectacled Cobra
Naja naja

This beautiful snake gets its name from the "spectacle" pattern on the back of its spread hood. It is valued for controlling rodents. They also consume birds, lizards, amphibians, and eggs. Their venom is used as an ingredient in painkillers and to treat certain cancers.

Crocodile Newt
Tylototriton shanjing

Commonly known as a crocodile newt, they are also called the emperor newt or mandarin salamander. They grow only about 15–20 cm long and look like tiny crocodiles. Crocodile newts are vividly coloured with an orange or yellow stripe running down the middle of their body, as well as an orange tail, limbs, and markings on the head. This colour pattern makes them very conspicuous and seemingly vulnerable to predation. However, the skin contains harmful toxins; therefore, the colour acts as a bright warning sign to predators to beware. They spend most of their time on land, entering the water for breeding. Their main area of distribution is along rivers in the mountains of Yunnan province in western China.

Wrinkled Hornbill
Aceros corrugatus

Hornbills spend almost all their time up in the trees, occasionally descending to pick up fallen fruit, their main source of food (mostly figs and nutmeg). They also eat lizards, snakes, rats, and nesting birds. Hornbills are known for their unusual nesting habits. After mating, the female retires to a hollow tree where she seals herself inside using dung and pellets of mud. With the help of the male, she plasters the entrance to the hole, leaving a tiny slit open to receive food from the male. During incubation (6–8 weeks), the female is fed by the male and moults all her feathers, becoming flightless for a time. Eventually, the female breaks out of the nest a week or more before the young are ready to leave the shelter. The young rebuild the entrance barrier, leaving a slit for feeding by both parents. When they are ready, the young birds break out on their own, with no help from their parents.

toronto **ZOO**

Sumatran Tiger
Panthera tigris sumatrae

The smallest and darkest of the tigers, Sumatrans have large, sharp, retractable claws and large canine teeth. On average, these tigers are 3 m long including the tail. The adult's weight ranges from 110 – 120 kg and cubs weigh about 1.5 kg at birth. In their native habitat, the tropical rain-forests of Sumatra, the tigers feed mainly on deer and wild pig but will also eat reptiles, birds, fish, berries, and carrion. The tiger's striped pattern creates camouflage: the black lines break up their body shape in tall grasslands. Their sense of vision and smell are very keen. Their hearing is very sensitive; cup-shaped ears help focus sound. They are fast and efficient swimmers. Their smaller size allows them to move quickly through the jungle. Solitary animals, Sumatran tigers usually come together only to mate or to share a kill.

The white spots on the back of a tiger's ears are called "eye spots" or "predator spots." It is believed that the spots function as false eyes and also make the tiger look larger to a predator approaching from behind, which helps the young cubs survive.

Conservation: Sumatran tigers are critically endangered. Despite legal protection, these tigers are still hunted. In the wild, as few as 400 remain and the species could be extinct in ten years. Captive breeding is the Sumatran tiger's only hope.

TORONTO ZOO'S PLANT COLLECTION

When visiting the Toronto Zoo, you will experience more than our amazing animals. The Zoo also has a vast and diverse plant collection of more than 3,000 species. One of the Zoo's aims is to recreate natural habitats of the world — equatorial rainforests in the African and Indo-Malaya Pavilions, woodlands, and a billabong in the Australasia Pavilion, and wetlands and tropical forest in the Americas Pavilion.

The tropical plant collection includes 400 trees, 4,000 shrubs, and endless ground cover. Many plants are grown from rare seeds obtained through the International Seed Exchange Program. Seeds from native species are collected in southern Ontario and exchanged for species from other countries, thereby increasing the diversity of the Zoo's plant collection.

Indo-Malayan Plants

Java Glory-bower
Clerodendrum speciosissimum, Verbena Family, Verbenaceae

Native to the islands of the Pacific, Java glory-bower is an impressive shrub with large leaves and beautiful orange-scarlet, nectar-bearing flowers. It is one of the many different butterfly plants that you will see in the Malayan Woods Pavilion. As you walk through this pavilion, butterflies float from flower to flower sipping nectar.

toronto ZOO

Bo Tree
Ficus religiosa,
Mulberry Family, Moraceae

Native to India and southeast Asia, this tree is considered sacred to Hindus and Buddhists. It is said that Buddha attained enlightenment under this species. Its large blue-green leaves are heart-shaped with long, drip-like tips. Drip tips allow excess water to run off the plant.

Hibiscus
Hibiscus rosa-sinensis,
Mallow Family,
Malvaceae

Originally native to Asia, this plant is now a common household plant all over the world. Many varieties have been cultivated with beautiful flowers from white to yellow, orange, pink, or red. It is also known as the "shoe flower" because the large flowers can be used to polish shoes!

Staghorn Fern
Platycerium bifurcatum,
Polypody Family,Polypodiaceae

This plant is an epiphyte meaning it is supported above the ground by resting on other plants. By attaching to a host plant high in the forest it is able to receive more sunlight, but no harm comes to the host plant. Staghorn ferns have two distinct leaf shapes: kidney-shaped leaves that are sterile and semi-upright antler-like leaves that are fertile. The brown fuzzy patches at the tips of the fertile leaves bear spores. When they are ripe, the spores release in the wind. A single plant can produce as many as 50 million spores in one season.

Bird's-Nest Fern
Asplenium nidus,
Asplenium Family,
Aspleniaceae

Another epiphytic fern is bird's-nest fern, native to tropical Asia. Its leaves are arranged in an upward-spreading, bowl-shaped rosette, giving this plant its name. The funnel-like leaf arrangement collects water and humus, providing nutrients to the roots. Its glossy, bright-green leaves can grow to be 50–150 cm long and 20 cm wide. This epiphyte can also grow on the ground.

Pied Imperial Pigeon

Pied Imperial Pigeon
Nicobar Ground Dove, Pheasant Pigeon

Pigeons and doves (Columbidae) have colonized almost every available habitat on Earth. They have a diet mainly composed of fruits and seeds, but some will eat insects and small animals. Pigeons do not drink by tipping their heads like other birds but keep their heads down and suck water in until they are finished.

Nicobar Ground Dove

Malayan Crested Fireback and Palawan Peacock Pheasants

Pheasants show strong sexual dimorphism where the males are bright and showy and the females duller and usually smaller than the males. They generally forage on the ground for greens, seeds, fruits, insects and small animals.

toronto ZOO

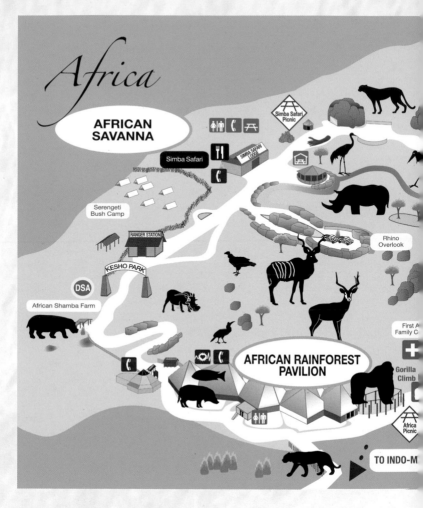

Africa

AFRICAN SAVANNA

Simba Safari Picnic

Simba Safari

SIMBA SAFARI LODGE

Serengeti Bush Camp

RANGER STATION

KESHO PARK

DSA

African Shamba Farm

Rhino Overlook

First A Family C

AFRICAN RAINFOREST PAVILION

Gorilla Climb

Africa Picnic

TO INDO-M

*A*frica has one of the largest and wildest animal populations in the world. The diverse landscape, from the endless plains of the Serengeti, to the high altitudes and tropical rainforests, is home to millions of plants and animals. The African Rainforest Pavilion is one of the largest indoor gorilla exhibits in North America. It features a two-acre African rainforest home for our

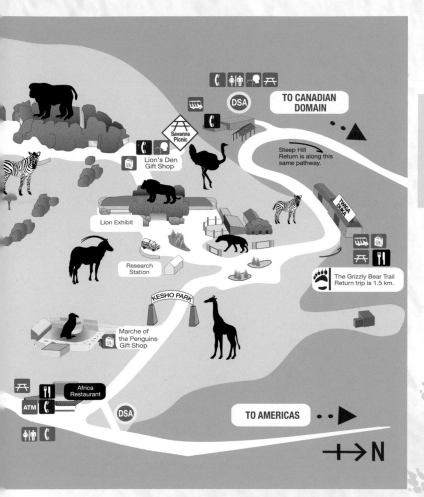

family of lowland gorillas. You'll also find the colourful Lake Malawi cichlids, dwarf crocodiles, ring-tailed lemurs and naked mole-rats. After leaving the rainforest you'll enter the savanna region of Kesho Park, a place where wildlife is seen amid the landscape features of East Africa. Zebras roam with the marabou storks and a rhinoceros looks on from nearby.

toronto ZOO

Western Lowland Gorilla
Gorilla gorilla gorilla

Lowland gorillas live in the rainforests of Central Africa. As you venture into the Gorilla Rainforest, you will see our gorilla family playing and socializing in their "rainforest re-creation" home (0.8 ha). Opened in 2001, the area gives the gorillas a place to play, interact with each other, and remain stimulated. It also gives visitors a chance to experience what the Central African rainforest environment is like, while discovering important conservation issues such as rainforest depletion and the bushmeat crisis.

Gorillas are the largest primate; males weigh an average of 175 kg and females 85 kg. Their muscular arms are longer than their short, thick legs. They walk on their feet and hands with their knuckles resting on the ground; however, they can walk bipedally (just their feet) for a short distance. Their coats are mainly black (their skin is also black), with the exception of the mature male who develops a silver-grey back. The high ridge on top of their heads is called a sagittal crest and is more prominent on the male than the female. Gorillas have vocalizations (grunts, barks, squeaks, etc.) that convey emotions or express approaching danger and give warnings to the intruders. Gorillas live in close-knit groups consisting of a dominant male, several females and their young, and sometimes, one or two other non-dominant males. The non-dominant males are probably sons of the dominant male and they will leave the family unit to start their own family or will eventually take over leadership. At night gorillas build nests to sleep in, which may be on the ground or in trees. Reproduction in gorillas is similar to humans. The gestation period is 265 days (about 9 months) and the baby is completely dependent on the mother for food and protection. Gorillas suffer from the same diseases as humans and will belch, cough, hiccup, sneeze, and yawn … just like us!

Drumming their chest is used as an alarm in the case of danger; however, it may also be done for the pure fun of it!

Conservation: Toronto Zoo supports gorilla conservation in several reserves in Central Africa and participates in other conservation efforts in the wild.

A Diversity of African Chameleons –
Meller's and Veiled Chameleons and their Nursery
Trioceros melleri
Chamaeleo calyptratus

Chameleons are well known for their ability to change colours. This "language of colour" communicates mood or fear, indicates willingness to breed, demonstrates when one is carrying eggs, or is used to defend

territory. Our exhibit includes a glimpse into the chameleon breeding centre and young chameleons that have hatched at Toronto Zoo.

With fingers placed to provide a tight grip on twigs and a tail that curls around branches, chameleons are well-adapted for life hunting in the branches of trees and shrubs. These lizards have a wonderful diversity of body shapes and adornments. The high cresst on the head of the male veiled chameleon is only one example.

Spotted-necked Otter
Lutra maculicollis

Some species of otters live both on the land and in the water; however, this endangered otter generally stays in its aquatic habitat. They are found in lakes, swamps, and rivers in the plains and mountains of sub-Saharan Africa. Spotted-necked otters live in family or bachelor groups of 6–10 animals. They are excellent swimmers and divers, diving fairly deep to look for food (fish, crabs, molluscs). Activity normally occurs in the early morning and late evening, except in areas where they are hunted, movements occur at night.

They make a variety of sounds (a "mew," "trill," or "whistle") to contact others or show their agitation or excitement.

toronto **ZOO**

West African Dwarf Crocodile
Osteolaemus tetraspis tetraspis

An endangered species, the dwarf crocodile inhabits the rainforests of western Africa. The crocodile is specially adapted for its aquatic habitat and lifestyle. Its ears and nose are waterproofed with special valves that close when submerged. They are also able to eat underwater without breathing water into their lungs. Their diet consists mostly of small fishes or other small vertebrates such as frogs. Adults tend to live as individuals, active usually only at dusk and during the night. This crocodile will grow to be about 1.5–1.8 m long.

Female dwarf crocodiles are good mothers to their young. They closely guard their eggs in carefully constructed mound nests of vegetation. After the eggs hatch, the female will stay with her young for several weeks.

Lake Malawi Cichlids
Cichlidae Family

These fishes are only found in Lake Malawi, the lake with the greatest number of different fish species in the world (Lake Malawi has over 700 fish species, Lake Ontario has only 68).

Although they are closely related, the cichlids of Lake Malawi have a remarkable degree of specialization. Different species have adapted to unique diets, habitats, and lifestyles with the evolution of different teeth, jaws, and bodies. These adaptations reduce competition for food and mates. Diets include algae (scraped off rocks), insects, and plankton. *Pseudotropheus demasoni* feeds on algae. Its slender body allows it to go into narrow fissures and feed in places inaccessible to other fish. *Fossorochromis rostratus,* a predator, sifts through sand to find invertebrates to consume. *Pseudotropheus saulosi* cultivates sandy areas to find diatoms (algae) to eat. *Cynotilapia afra* feeds on plankton near its rocky habitat. The cichlids of Lake Malawi are brightly coloured fish. These colours are signals to others of their own kind.

AFRICAN RIVER FISHES

Many long rivers flow through Africa, including the Nile River, which is the longest river in the world (6,700 km). Other major rivers in Africa are the Niger, Congo, and Zambezi. All the rivers share similar characteristics — mostly, they are dark, warm, and murky. The fish that inhabit these rivers have adapted to living and thriving in these conditions.

The **African lungfish** (*Protopterus annectens*) have adapted to living in regions that experience dry and rainy seasons. In the dry season, lungfish bury themselves in a muddy burrow. Inside the burrow, they secrete mucus, which coats their body, forming a cocoon. They are still able to breathe through an opening in the cocoon. Once the rains start, the mud around the cocoon is washed away, allowing the fish to emerge. The lungfish needs to breathe air every 30–60 minutes.

The **African bonytongue** (*Heterotis niloticus*) is also able to breathe air. This ability allows it to inhabit the oxygen-poor waters that are common in tropical areas. Bonytongues tend to live along the river bottom. They come to the surface to gulp air when supplemental air is needed. To feed, bonytongues sift sediments using a vacuum motion, looking for worms, snails and other bottom-dwelling species.

Generally, these river fishes have brown or dull colouring, that helps to camouflage them in the muddy waters of their habitat. The murkiness of the water creates poor visibility, so the fish must find other ways to navigate and hunt in the rivers. Some fish use their acute sense of smell; others use alternative methods such as the electricity of the **elephantnose mormyrid** (*Gnathonemus petersii*). The mormyrid is a fish that uses electric impulses to navigate in the dark or murky waters. The electric impulses send back signals that the fish can interpret, identifying objects or other fish in the water. Unlike the electric eel, the mormyrid's electric current is not strong enough to stun its pray.

toronto ZOO

Slender-tailed Meerkat
Suricata suricatta

Meerkats are long and slender with dark bands across the back of their brownish fur. The colour of their fur helps them to camouflage in their habitat of open bush and savanna. They have four digits on each foot with very sharp, non-retractable, curved claws. Meerkats live in family groups of about 40 individuals headed by a dominant female and male. Each individual has a specific role in the group such as standing on the lookout, babysitting the young, or foraging for food. They have a good sense of hearing and smell; they also have good eyesight but have trouble with depth perception. Their claws are used as burrowing tools, helping to construct their underground chambers. Consisting of entrance holes, tunnels, and sleeping chambers, the burrow system may have up to 70 different entrances.

Meerkats have a white membrane located between the eye and eyelid that acts as a windshield wiper, removing sand from their eyes with every blink!

Aba Aba
Gymnarchus niloticus

The aba aba lives in swamps and oxbow lakes, anywhere with still, muddy water conditions. It has a compressed looking body with a very long dorsal fin along its back from head to tail. Their eyes are very small; however, they have another device to help them see. The aba aba possesses weak electric organs located near the end of the tail on each side of the body. They rest very quietly and produce an electrical field around themselves, sending out pulses. The fish will then detect any disturbances that take place when the signals are sent out. From these disturbances they can identify prey, predators, their own species, and other objects around them. The young eat insects and other invertebrates; adults feed on fish.

The aba aba can move equally well forwards or backwards using their especially long dorsal fin.

Sacred Ibis
Threskiornis aethiopicus

These long-beaked birds live throughout Africa, India, and Australia. They are commonly found on the upper Nile River and in the rest of Africa in swamps and on large lakes. They use their long, curved bills to retrieve invertebrates, fish, and amphibians from muddy riverbanks. The adult's head and neck are bare with black skin. Young ibises are born covered in white feathers, but they develop adult plumage by their third year. They like to live, hunt, and breed in groups of their own species, and also with other water birds.

In ancient Egypt this bird was worshipped by many people, and its long, down-curved beak can be found among the hieroglyphs on ancient Egyptian monuments.

Pygmy Hippopotamus
Hexaprotodon liberiensis

Similar in appearance to a river hippo, the pygmy hippo is a considerably smaller version. There are some differences in the face — the eyes are set on the side of the head, the head is rounder and not so broad and flat, and the nostrils are large and circular — however, most features are similar, just smaller. Pygmy hippos live in dense, swampy forests and are less aquatic than river hippos, spending most of their time on land. They sleep during the day near rivers and streams and search for food (various terrestrial and aquatic vegetation) in the late evening. They are excellent swimmers and are able to walk on the river bottom. Pygmy hippos are solitary, except when they are with their young or come together for mating. They avoid crossing paths with other pygmy hippos and will fight each other if an encounter occurs. Serious injuries may result from sharp canine teeth.

toronto ZOO

Ring-tailed Lemur
Lemur catta

Lemurs are primates that are found only on the island of Madagascar off the southeast coast of Africa. Although they are often found climbing trees, they spend more time on the ground than any other lemur, so they are often called terrestrial. They move by walking or running quadrupedally, holding their tails almost completely vertically as they move. They have a herbivorous diet, consisting of various plants and fruits and often lick rain and morning dew from leaves as a water source. Due to the clearing of trees and the destruction of their habitat, ring-tailed lemurs are an endangered species.

Nile Softshell Turtle
Trionyx triunguis

When inactive or buried in the sand, softshell turtles can stay underwater for prolonged periods. Softshells pump water into their throats where blood vessels absorb oxygen directly from the water. If quietly submerged, this turtle can absorb 70% of its oxygen requirements through its skin. For protection and as an ambush method, they sit covered in sand with just their snout sticking out of the substrate. Nile softshell turtles are curious, intelligent and active turtles. They use their long necks and nose for investigating new objects and in courtship - the amorous male lovingly biting the female's neck. Toronto Zoo has contributed to research that demonstrates that these turtles are one of the few reptile species that will play with objects.

A DIVERSISTY OF AFRICAN TORTOISES

Hingeback Tortoise
Kinixys homeana

Some turtles have a hinge on the lower shell but hingeback tortoises are the only ones with a hinge on the upper shell! The tortoise scrapes a shallow depression in leaves or forest debris and rests with the shell closed, an effective defense against even the most determined predator.

Radiated Tortoise
Astrochelys radiata

Named for the radiating yellow lines on the shell, the radiated tortoise is one of the world's rarest, and most attractive, tortoises. They are most active after rains when they feed on grasses, fruit, and succulent plants.

Madagascar Pyxie Tortoise
Pyxis sp.

This small endangered tortoise is active during the rainy season foraging for mushrooms, leaves, and flowers.

Conservation: Toronto Zoo supports turtle conservation projects in Madagascar including community-based habitat conservation, environmental education programs, and projects that promote traditional practices that once protected tortoises. We are part of a global program to breed tortoises as part of a captive assurance population.

toronto ZOO

Nile Monitor
Varanus niloticus

The Nile monitor is the largest lizard in Africa; fully grown it can mea-sure up to 1.5 m. They live along rivers, lakes, and swamps near rainforests. Their diet consists of a wide variety of foods such as crabs, frogs, fish, small reptiles, mammals, and birds. They are excellent swimmers, and if they are disturbed or threatened, they will dive into the water and remain submerged or swim away until it is safe to resurface. Their skin ranges in colour from dark black to olive green to yellow in a beautiful and intricate design. Females lay an average of 35 eggs in the ground. After 9–10 months, the eggs hatch and the young break out of the mound in search of the closest water source.

Naked Mole-rat
Heterocephalus glaber

Native Africans have known about naked mole-rats for a long time; however, they weren't discovered by the western world until the 1970s. The reason they weren't discovered any earlier is because they spend most of their time underground; rarely will they make an appearance above ground. These fascinating creatures are rodents without pigmentation. Their ears are small holes in the skin with no external flaps, and they are virtually blind. They also have two pairs of long, protruding incisor teeth. Naked mole-rats are "eusocial" animals, which means they live in highly structured co-operative colonies much like bees and ants. A queen resides over the colony and will breed with only a few select males. Other adult females are not permitted to breed. The rest of the colony works together to raise the young and maintain the colony that ranges in size from 20–300 individuals. The colony is a complex underground burrow system. Mole-rats dig the tunnels with their incisor teeth, communicating by touch, smell, and noises.

FROGS: A CHORUS OF COLOUR

Tomato Frog
Dyscophus guineti

Tomato frogs are named for the bright red color that serves as a warning. When threatened, a tomato frog puffs up its body to look larger and oozes a toxic, sticky, white substance from its skin that is used as a defence against predators. Unfortunately, in Madagascar these colours are fading quickly. Habitat destruction is the largest threat frogs face, but collection of frogs for the pet trade has impacted wild populations.

Mantella Frog
Mantella sp.

Mantella frogs are among the most brightly coloured of all frogs. Most *Mantella* species have the same toxins found in the South American poison dart frogs.

Conservation: A focus on conserving biodiversity may help secure the future for these beautiful frogs and Toronto Zoo supports local breeding programmes in Madagascar.

Gaboon Viper
Bitis gabonica

The gaboon viper is one of Africa's most beautiful snakes. The stout body is boldly patterned which provides excellent camouflage and allows this sluggish viper to become nearly invisible among leaves of the forest floor.

Unseen, it lies motionless in wait along forest trails to ambush birds and small mammals as they pass by. It is the heaviest venomous snake in Africa, weighing 8 kg, and grows to a length of 2 metres. The gaboon viper also possesses the longest fangs of any snake, measuring up to 4 cm long.

toronto ZOO

Royal python
Python regius

Royal pythons are named for their attractive pattern and rich chocolate brown colour. The name royal refers to the belief that Cleopatra wore these snakes around her wrists. These snakes are also referred to as ball pythons because they curl into a tight ball when threatened. Our animal care staff identify these snakes by recognizing the unique pattern each snake's head.

Warthog
Phacochoerus africanus

Warthogs may not be known for their good looks; however, they play an important role on the savanna. Living in the sub-Saharan grasslands, warthogs graze the land feeding on grasses, roots, seeds, and fruit. Both the male and female have four tusks at the side of their snouts. The upper tusks

curve upwards, while the lower tusks are shorter and much sharper, and are used for defence when necessary. The tusks are continuously growing canine teeth. At night and midday, the warthogs lie in a den (under a rock or in a cave). The young enter first, followed by the adults who push themselves in backwards to defend the entrance with their tusks.

Lack of hair makes warthogs vulnerable in extreme heat, so they seek relief by rolling in the mud. The mud covering also serves as camouflage and keeps insects from biting.

Red River Hog
Potamochoerus porcus

The red river hog is mostly reddish in colour, however, they also have a white facial mask, white whiskers, long black and white tufts at the tip of their ears and a white mane that stands up along the length of the spine. The tufts on their ears and the mane along their back greatly increase the perceived size of the pig when fluffed out. On average they weigh about 45 kg. Both sexes have tusks. Red river hogs are found in Africa from Senegal to northern and eastern Zaire, wherever there is enough rainfall to maintain dense vegetation and keep the ground moderately soft. They are most active at night and rest by day in burrows they dig themselves. Diet consists mainly of roots, berries and fruits, although reptiles, eggs and occasionally young birds are also eaten. Red river hogs can swim both above water and below. They also have an outstanding sense of smell and can run quite fast.

toronto ZOO

Marabou Stork
Leptoptilos crumeniferus

You will see these peculiar-looking birds roaming among the zebras in Toronto Zoo's Kesho Park, much like they would in their African homeland. The marabou stork is one of the largest flying birds in the world; its wingspan can be as wide as 2.9 m. On the ground, they measure 1.5 m tall. Their head is sunk into their shoulders, giving them a hunched posture. They are scavenger birds, feeding on carrion (animal carcasses) and small animals. These ravenous feeders often wait with vultures at a lion's kill.

Storks clatter their large bills together to greet their partners.

Masai Giraffe
Giraffa camelopardalis tippelskirchi

Masai giraffes are found in the southern half of Kenya and Tanzania where they live in the open savanna and wooded grasslands. Females grow to be 4.3–4.6 m tall and males are slightly taller at 4.6–5.4 m. Their necks are 1.5 m or more in length and contain seven elongated vertebrae (the same number of vertebrae found in a human's neck!) attached to one another by ball and socket joints, making the neck very flexible. Their long necks are an adaptation that allows them to feed high in the trees. Along with their oversized necks, giraffes also have large hearts and long tongues. The heart weighs about 11.5 kg and pumps approximately 60 L of blood per minute, compared to the 4 1/2 L per minute pumped by a human's heart. The tongue is black, about 45.6 cm long, and used for plucking leaves from trees. Generally, a giraffe will give birth to only one offspring at a time. Birth takes place standing up so the calf has a long drop to the ground once it arrives (about 1.6 m). After about 20 minutes, the young are able to stand up on their long and shaky legs. Full size is attained at 5 years old for females and age 7 for males. Masai giraffes have an acute sense of smell and hearing, and extremely keen eyesight; their height gives them a great range of vision. Giraffes live in herds of 30–40 individuals, spending most of their day (16–20 hours) feeding, consuming up to 64 kg of fresh leafy food per day. They can go without water for several weeks but can drink 45 L at one time.

The giraffe is the world's tallest animal.

toronto ZOO

South African Ostrich
Struthio camelus australis

This tallest of all birds (up to 2.4 m) cannot fly. However, it can run faster than any other two-legged animal, up to 80 km/h. Cheetahs are the only predator that can outrun the ostrich; however, the ostrich has more endurance than a cheetah. The South African ostrich feeds mostly on vegetable matter but will also eat some invertebrates. They are strong birds whose powerful kicks can seriously injure predators. Their eyesight is excellent as their eyes are huge — approximately the size of a tennis ball! Ostriches often associate with other animals in their habitat to detect predators. Zebras, and other hoofed animals, have a keener sense of smell than ostriches, who have keener eyesight, thus producing a useful combination for warning each other of danger.

The ostrich is the only bird that has two toes; all other birds have three or four.

Spotted Hyena
Crocuta crocuta

The spotted hyena is the largest of the hyena family and has a big head, skinny legs, and a sloping back. Hyenas live and hunt in packs. They have an excellent sense of sight, smell, and hearing. They have strong front paws for holding down a carcass while they tear off the meat. As well, their jaws are so strong they can crush and chew up bone, and their teeth are able to cut hide and tendons; thus, they are able to eat all parts of their prey. Their stomach produces very acidic secretions that enable them to digest bones and their droppings may be white and crusty because of the bone in them. Other indigestible items such as horns, hooves, and hair are regurgitated.

Sable Antelope
Hippotragus niger niger

The sable antelope is dark in colour with heavily ringed horns that arch over its head. Sable antelopes travel in herds, consisting of one male and 10–20 females and offspring. Young males leave the herd at 2 years old to join a bachelor herd. When a herd becomes too large, the dominant male loses control and the bachelors steal the young females, forming a new herd. Females also struggle for dominance in the herd, and the highest-ranking female generally initiates most herd movements. If needed, sable antelopes can run up to 57 km/h. They always run in a bunch, never single file. Because of their size they have few enemies.

toronto ZOO

African Crested Porcupine
Hystrix africaeaustralis

The name porcupine originates from the old French words porc "pig" and espin "spiny". African crested porcupines are only found in Sub-Saharan Africa. They primarily live in habitat with rocky outcroppings and hillsides. They use burrows for shelter. They feed on roots, tubers and bulbs and will sometimes gnaw on bark or bones. They are covered in black bristly hairs, sharp quills (up to 30 cm long) and spines (up to 50 cm long). Hollow spines on the porcupine's tail rattle when shaken. Porcupines do not throw their quills, but make a "reverse-charge" to drive the quills into their attacker. They have good hearing and will freeze when approached by predators such as big cats, large birds, and hyenas.

African Lions
Panthera leo

African lions live south of the Sahara Desert to South Africa, except the Congo. Unlike all other cats, lions hunt in groups with the lionesses doing the hunting. Male African lions are huge weighing between 149 kg and 249 kg and have a distinct mane. Lions are more social than any other cat, living in groups (prides) of up to 30 individuals. Although they may be the King of the Beasts, they are in great danger from their only enemy, humans.

In 2012, the Toronto Zoo welcomed three new white lions as a permanent addition to to the African Savanna family. Unique to the Timbavati region of South Africa, these rare and beautiful cats have not been seen in the wild in over 15 years. They carry the recessive gene known as a colour inhibitor of the Kruger subspecies of lion *(Panthera leo krugeri)*. With African lion populations dwindling, they are now classified as a vulnerable species, and soon may be listed as endangered. Come see our white lions, catch a daily Keeper Talk and help the Zoo bring awareness to the plight of the African lion in the wild!

A lion's hearty roar can be heard up to 9 km away.

Olive Baboon
Papio cynocephalus anubis

Olive baboons are commonly found in African savanna regions in large groups or "troops." Generally, the baboons live in troops of 100–200 animals organized in a strict hierarchy of both males and females. Females form the core of a group and spend their whole lives with the same troop; males often transfer to different groups. The female rank within the troop is family-based; thus, a daughter will inherit her mother's rank. A troop's range will cover anywhere from 400–4,000 ha. Baboons are omnivorous (they eat both plants and animals). Their diet consists of a variety of items including grass, leaves, grasshoppers, lizards, frogs, small rodents, and young antelope.

Adult baboons spend much of their time grooming. If two females are grooming an adult male simultaneously, they will begin to scream and fight until one withdraws.

Grevy's Zebra
Equus grevyi

Grevy's zebras roam the open plains and grasslands of central and east Africa. Most often they are seen grazing, as they spend about 60 percent of their day eating. Grevy's zebras are the largest of all the zebras, and their stripes are narrow and closely set together. The zebra's distinctive stripes are actually a method of camouflage; when the zebra is moving, the stripes create a disruptive pattern that confuses predators. Zebras rely on their acute sense of sight and hearing. Their eyes are set far back on their head, which gives them a wide field of view. Their long legs help the zebra run fast, giving them speed as a defence against predators.

Each individual zebra has its own distinctive stripe pattern.

Conservation: Grevy's zebras are an endangered species that has been protected in the wild and bred in captivity to preserve the species.

toronto **ZOO**

Cheetah
Acinonyx jubatus jubatus

Found widely distributed throughout Africa, these cats are known for their speed. In fact, cheetahs are the fastest land mammal in the world and have many different adaptations for running. Cheetahs have a large heart, over-sized liver, enlarged nostrils, and flexible spine. Its large eyes, positioned on a small, flat face, allow for maximum binocular vision. The cheetah's tail acts as a stabilizer when running at high speeds. The maximum speed (80–112 km/h) can only be maintained for a few hundred metres. As the cheetah runs, only one foot at a time touches the ground, and at two points during their stride no feet touch the ground. Before ambushing its prey, a cheetah will stalk it from a distance of about 70–100 m. Cheetahs mostly eat small gazelles and the young of other antelopes.

White Rhinoceros
Ceratotherium simum simum

White rhinos are the second largest living land animal after the elephant. Males weigh as much as 3,600 kg. The name "white" rhino is believed to have derived from the Afrikaans word widje, which means "wide," referring to its broad, square-lipped mouth. A white rhino's horns (they have two) are made of keratin, the same material that makes up human hair and nails. The horn continues to grow throughout the rhino's life, but is generally worn down by the animal to keep it from getting too long. If the horn is broken off, a new one will start to grow. The white rhino has a keen sense of hearing and smell, but its vision is relatively poor.

All rhinos are threatened or endangered. The white rhino is the most numerous but they are very threatened, generally because they are hunted for their horns. Poaching has increased dramatically and they could soon become extinct.

Southern Ground Hornbill
Bucorvus leadbeateri

Ground hornbills are large birds with black feathers, characteristic red facial skin, and long eyelashes. Preferring to live in groups of 2–12  individuals, they cover and aggressively defend large territories up to 100 sq. km. Groups usually consist of a dominant breeding pair with helpers of various ages. Ground hornbills are the largest co-operative breeding birds in the world. Sometimes an individual (usually a male) will not breed, although sexually capable; instead he helps the dominant pair raise their young. Ground hornbills spend most of their time searching their savanna habitat for food. Predominantly carnivorous, they feed on a large range of insects, reptiles, amphibians, and small- to medium-size mammals.

White-headed Vulture
Trigonoceps occipitalis

These scavengers will often arrive immediately after a predator has killed its prey. White-headed vultures are called "clean" feeders because they don't get any blood on their feathers when they feed. Despite arriving first to the kill (carcasses of large mammals), they tend to feed on scraps that other raptors drop. They will also eat birds and young or injured antelope. Their "white" head is actually bare skin, which blushes red when they are excited or angry. The white-headed vulture's beak is red with a black tip; their bodies are covered in dark feathers with a white crest. The claws are black and the grip is stronger than other vultures. The white-headed vulture's wingspan is 2.3 m.

toronto ZOO

Greater Kudu
Tragelaphus strepsiceros

Roaming the open forests in the African savanna, the greater kudu is one of the largest antelope species on the continent. They are also considered to be one of the most handsome because of the male's long, spiralled horns. The female kudu is hornless; however, they both have vertical white stripes on their bodies and white markings under their eyes. The markings help to provide camouflage for the kudu: when standing still, they blend into the background and are barely visible. They are also excellent leapers, clearing bushes 2–3 m high, and are powerful swimmers.

Males will sometimes fight to a mutual death as a result of their horns locking during combat.

River Hippopotamus
Hippopotamus amphibius

In the summertime at the Zoo, the hippopotami will likely be submerged underwater, with only their eyes, ears, and nostrils visible. They spend two-thirds of their day underwater as their skin is sensitive to the sun and may crack if exposed for too long. When out of the water, the hippo's skin oozes moisture that contains a red pigment and, therefore, has been termed "blood sweat." Hippo teeth are actually quite large, and the incisors and canines are ivory. Generally, they live in groups of up to 30 members with one dominant male. A group of hippos is called a "bloat".

Although the hippopotamus appears to have naked skin, it is actually covered in fine, short hairs.

African Penguin
Spheniscus demersus

African penguins are found on the coast and islands of southern Africa and Namibia. This is the only penguin species which breeds in Africa. They spend a great percentage of their lives at sea. They feed primarily

on shoaling pelagic fish such as anchovies, pilchards (sardines), horse mackerel, and round herrings, supplemented by squid and crustaceans. Although they form vast breeding colonies, these birds are monogamous. Pairs bond together and will return to the same breeding sites year after year. Two eggs are usually laid with the male and female participating equally in the incubation duties. African penguins have developed unique adaptations to life in the temperate zone and their entire body is densely covered with close packed feathers that overlap like tiles, forming a waterproof outer shell. The major current threat to these birds has come from humans, namely oil pollution and competition with commercial fisheries for food. As of 1999, there are estimated to be 224,000 individuals.

Starlings

Unlike the starlings we see in Canada, many species are extremely colourful in Africa. Starlings eat a broad spectrum of foods. In Africa, reproduction is dependent on the availability of large quantities of insects.

toronto **ZOO**

TORONTO ZOO'S GREENHOUSES

In early 1973 the Zoo started to assemble its enormous plant collection. Planting of the pavilions started in January 1974 and was completed in June of the same year. Zoo horticulturists chose tropical plants from 30 nurseries in Florida after extensive research to ensure geographical authenticity. The plants were stored at a central point in Florida until the pavilions were completed. They were then shipped from Florida directly to Toronto on special climate-controlled trucks.

Three greenhouses are maintained on site to propagate and grow plants for exhibits. Since there is a high mortality rate of botanicals in exhibits due to animal interference and low light levels, a constant exchange of plants takes place between the pavilions and the greenhouses. The greenhouse is also used as a plant hospital for injured specimens.

Africa Plants

Mountain Thistle
Acanthus montanus,
Acanthus Family, Acanthaceae

Found in western tropical Africa, this plant has thistle-like leaves with very sharp spines. The mountain thistle grows to a height of 2 m, with dark-green, deeply lobed leaves and white or pale-pink flowers.

Fiddle-leaf Fig
Ficus lyrata, Mulberry Family, Moraceae

This fast-growing tree has spectacular, leathery, fiddle-shaped leaves and reddish-brown bark. Found in tropical Africa, this tree and tiny gall wasps depend solely on one another for reproduction. In spring, figs form at the branch tips. Fiddle-leaf figs grow to a height of 12 m.

Sausage Tree
Kigelia africana, Bignonia Family, Bignoniaceae

This tree produces beautiful, trumpet-shaped, dark-maroon flowers with yellow veins. These blooms, along with a sausage-shaped fruit, hang from rope-like stalks that grow to be a few metres long. The flowers are pollinated by bats that are attracted to their unpleasant smell. In Africa, the pulp of the fruit is mixed with sugar, honey, and water to make beer.

Bird of Paradise
Strelitzia reginae, Strelitzia Family, Strelitziaceae

This plant is known for its dramatically shaped and brightly coloured flowers that emerge from a boat-like sheath over a period of several days. Native to southern Africa, it received its name because the flower resembles the beak and head plumage of a bird. The leaves are also very beautiful with a pale grey-blue underside.

Cycads
Encephalartos hildebrandtii, Zamia Family, Zamiaceae

Cycads are primitive plants, often described as living fossils. They have been around since the dinosaurs, and little has changed in their structure. They can survive in almost every kind of habitat, preferring bright sun. Cycads are restricted to tropical and subtropical regions of the

world that receive moderate to high rainfall. All cycad species produce brightly coloured cones and seeds. Their leaves are large, stiff, and palm-like.

toronto ZOO

Canadian Domain

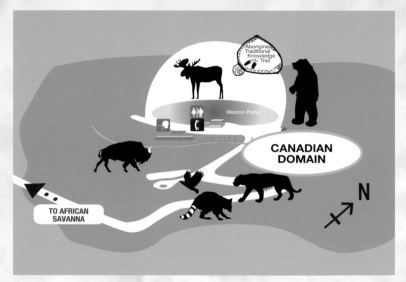

*C*anada is a large and diverse country represented by many geographic regions: boreal forests, a temperate coastal rainforest, mountains, vast grassy plains, a small desert, Arctic tundra, and glacial ice. At the Zoo, the Canadian Domain is situated in an impressive valley, carved out by the meandering Rouge River that crosses the site. Here you'll find wood bison roaming the open plains, grizzly bears playing in the sun, and bald eagles perched high above. You will also see extraordinary moose, cougars, elk, and raccoons.

Canada Lynx
Lynx canadensis

The Canada lynx is found in boreal forests of Canada, Alaska, and the northern portions of the United States. Its distribution essentially mirrors that of the snowshoe hare, its principal prey. Because of this very close predator-prey relationship with snowshoe hare, population densities fluctuate dramatically with the prey cycle. Lynx populations peak one to two years after the cyclic 10-year peak in snowshoe hare numbers. They may travel up to 1,200 km in search of areas where snowshoe hares are in abundance. They also prey on small rodents, birds and deer. Locally Canada lynx are endangered, but generally populations are healthy. They are mostly terrestrial and nocturnal, but may be found moving about at any time of the day.

American Moose
Alces alces americana

Moose are the largest member of the deer family. The largest of the moose species are found in North America; European moose are known as elk and are smaller in size. Found in northern Canada, Alaska, and parts of northern Europe and Asia, moose inhabit areas along lakes and streams in forested areas (deciduous, coniferous, and tundra regions). Moose are very comfortable in the water. Aquatic plants make up their summer diet, along with leaves and twigs; however, in the winter they are left with only twigs, shrubs, and willow bark. Their eyesight is very poor — to compensate, they have an acute sense of smell and hearing. In the summer a moose's coat is rich in colour, ranging from dark brown to black, red, and grey. Its winter coat is thicker than in the summer, but duller in colour (grey-brown).

toronto ZOO

Cougar
Puma concolor

Also known as a puma, mountain lion, or panther, the cougar is a large cat found in western North and South America. They move with great agility and are excellent climbers. Cougars also have great jumping power; they can leap up 6 m from the ground into a tree. To catch their prey, the cougar will jump onto the animal's back and, using its long canine teeth and strong jaws, kill it with a bite on the neck. Cougars tend to stalk their prey using the element of surprise instead of simply chasing after their food. The cougar has long hind limbs in proportion to its fore limbs, which helps it to jump and move about easily in steep, rocky areas. A cougar's diet consists of a variety of large mammals, preferably deer, but they also eat bighorn sheep, mountain goats, porcupine, beaver, and other small mammals.

Grizzly Bear
Ursus arctos horribilis

Grizzly bears are often seen walking slowly with their heads slung low, swinging from side to side, following the same well-beaten track. This gives no indication of how quickly they can move with great stamina. Grizzlies are large, powerful bears that can reach as high as 3 m when standing up, and they weigh anywhere from 102–324 kg. Their diet changes with the seasons, their age, and their state of health. Being omnivorous, they feed on both plants and animals. On the Pacific coast they stand in rivers during the salmon spawning and eat salmon, one after another. As the food supply dwindles in October, grizzly bears start to appear lethargic, sending a hormone trigger to their bodies that they are ready to become dormant. When they enter the dormancy state, their heart rate and respiration drop, but there is only a slight drop in body temperature. They awake in the spring when the melting snow floods them out. Grizzlies tend to live solitary lives, except for a mother and her cubs, but large groups will occasionally gather together at major food sources (salmon streams).

American Elk
Cervus elaphus canadensis

The name American elk is interchangeable with the name wapiti, which is the Shawnee word for "white rump." They do, indeed, have a large white-coloured patch on their rump. The rest of their body ranges from light to dark brown. Only the males carry a grand set of antlers. These large and heavy antlers (160–145 cm, averaging 13 kg) begin to grow in April. Over the summer, the antlers are covered in a live, blood-carrying tissue called velvet. By the end of the summer, most of the velvet is rubbed off, leaving them with a shiny and hard rack in the fall. This set of antlers is shed in February or March before a new set grows again in April. Within the deer family, elk are the second largest in size (after the moose). They are fast runners, reaching speeds up to 50 km/h, as well as good swimmers. Elk are strictly herbivorous, grazing on grass, weeds, flowers, and mushrooms in the summer and woody browse and twigs in the winter. Work is being done to reintroduce elk to southern Ontario.

Wood Bison
Bison bison athabascae

Listed as endangered in 1878, there is only one wild herd of wood bison remaining in the world; they can be found in the Northwest Territories of Canada. There are also a few small captive herds living in northern Alberta. These huge animals can weigh as much as 1,350 kg. They are covered in brownish-black hair with a coat of dense shaggy hair around the head and neck, creating beards as long as 30 cm. Wood bison shed their thick hair early in the summer. During the time it takes for the fur to grow back, they wallow in marshes and dust bowls to coat their skin and keep biting flies out.

Wood bison calves are generally born in the spring. When the cow is ready to give birth, she will leave the herd, give birth, and then rejoin the herd with the calf as soon as it can run, which is in about 3 hours! By the fall, the young calf has gained enough strength to run with the herd.

Conservation: Toronto Zoo has participated in the wood bison recovery program since 1977. The herd grew quickly and beginning in 1985 groups of wood bison born at the Toronto Zoo were returned to the wild. These formed a new wild herd in the Waterhen Reserve in Manitoba and contributed to the Yukon Wood Bison Projects. In 1988 wood bison were downlisted from Endangered to Threatened. There are now more than 3,000 wood bison in wild herds.

toronto ZOO

Trumpeter Swan
Olor buccinator

Trumpeter swans are the rarest swans in the world, as well as the largest. With its neck and legs outstretched, it can measure nearly 2 m from bill to feet. Their wingspan length varies with sex and age; in adults, it can reach 2–2.5 m. Adult swans become flightless for about a month when they moult (shed their feathers) in the summer. However, males and females have adapted to moult at different times so there is always an adult who is able to fly while the other parent stays with the young. Trumpeter swans feed on aquatic plants, insects, small fish and snails. They use their long necks and strong bills to pull up plants from underwater that other birds can't reach. Their name comes from the trumpet-like call that they make.

 Conservation: Toronto Zoo has participated in a successful program to reintroduce Trumpeter Swans in Ontario.

Northern Bald Eagle
Haliaeetus leucocephalus

These "bald" eagles are often seen looking majestic, perched high in the trees. The bald eagle's head, neck, and tail are white; the rest of its plumage is dark brown. The white colouring is found only on adults after 4 to 6 years of age; immature birds are black in colour. Their beak and feet are bright yellow. Bald eagles have strong populations on both Canadian coasts and are also found (in more limited quantities) throughout the rest of USA and Canada. In the wild, eagles are usually found near a water source, where they catch the majority of their food. About 60 percent of their diet is fish. Along with grizzly bears, bald eagles also take part in the salmon spawning, feeding on the fish "die-off." The eagles watch the water source from the trees and swoop down on their prey when the timing is right. Their wingspan is 2.2 m.

 Conservation: Bald eagles in southern Ontario are recovering due to reintroduction efforts assisted by the Toronto Zoo.

Tundra

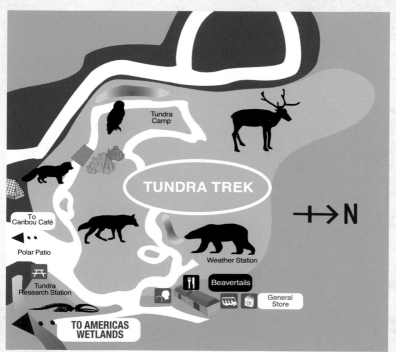

*T*he word tundra comes from the Finnish word tunturia, meaning treeless plain. Tundra in the northern hemisphere encircles the North Pole and extends south to the coniferous forests. Below the thin layer of soil lies the permafrost, a permanently frozen layer of ground. This is a land of water – up to 50 % of the surface is covered with shallow lakes, rivers, streams, bogs and fens.

The Arctic tundra is relatively low in biodiversity. For instance there are only 48 species of land mammals living here. However in the summer, many animals migrate to the tundra to take advantage of the abundant plants, insects and fish.

At the Zoo be sure to visit this area and see majestic polar bears through underwater viewing, try howling with the wolves, drop into the weather station, or explore teepees on the Tundra – and more!

toronto ZOO

Reindeer
Rangifer tarandus tarandus

Found in the tundra of northern Europe and Asia, the reindeer has a thick coat to keep it warm in the cold Arctic air. The undercoat is protected by hollow hairs, which provide insulation and warmth. Their long hooves act as snowshoes when walking over the snow and prevent them from sinking. Reindeer generally live to be about 15 years old.

Reindeer (known as caribou in North America) are the only species of deer in which both sexes have antlers. The antlers are used to spar with rivals, clear snow, get food, and defend against wolves. Caribou are decreasing rapidly in the wild in Canada.

Arctic Fox
Alopex lagopus

This fox lives on the lands of the circumpolar Arctic. It has furry soles, short ears, and a short muzzle – all adaptations to survive the harsh Arctic temperatures that can dip as low as -50°C. During the summer their coats are brown or gray to match the colour of their tundra habitat. Blending in helps them effectively hunt rodents, birds, and even fish. In winter their coats turn white. Prey can be hard to find during the harsh winters so a fox may follow the region's top predator - the polar bear - and clean up any scraps leftover from its kill.

The Arctic fox has more young per litter than any other wild mammal in the world – up to 14!

Arctic Wolf
Canis lupus hudsonicus

Arctic wolves are major predators in their territories. They eat large mammals such as deer, moose, and caribou, as well as small mammals (mice, rabbits), birds, fish, and insects. Their habitat depends on the caribou; the wolves follow migrating caribou over 500 km from the Arctic tundra in summer to the boreal woods of northern Canada in the winter. Wolves are very social and prefer to live in packs for protection and hunting. To take down a caribou, the wolves circle the herd or work in relays. They may make as many as 30 chases before making a kill. Wolves use their keen sense of smell and hearing to detect prey. When they howl, they may be communicating with others in the pack, rounding up a scattered pack, marking their territories, or warning wolves from different packs to leave their territory (which they guard closely); their howl can be heard up to 5 km away.

Snowy Owl
Bubo scandiacus

Adult males are almost pure white; adult females and juveniles have white feathers marked with brown bars. Females are larger than males. Owls must swivel their heads to a follow a moving object because their eyes do not move in their sockets. Unlike most owls, the snowy owl is active during the day. This adaptation is not surprising given that daylight is continuous within the Arctic Circle during breeding season.

toronto ZOO

Lesser Snow Goose
Chen caerulescens

This goose has two different appearances: a white phase and a blue phase – subsets of the same species. The head can be stained rusty brown from the minerals in the soil where they feed. The lesser snow goose population has grown steadily over the past 50 years. A number of factors have contributed to this increase: an abundant diet of agricultural crops such as rice, corn and winter wheat along the migratory route improves survival rates; and climate change, especially in the Arctic, allows for earlier nesting and greater chick survival. On the flip side, these larger populations mean breeding sites and migration routes can quickly become stripped of traditional food sources, and overcrowding increases their susceptibility to illness.

Polar Bear
Ursus maritimus

Polar bears are the largest land carnivores in the world. Males weigh anywhere from 300–800 kg and females are approximately 150–300 kg. They live along Arctic coastlines, frequenting the broken edges of ice packs. Their fur is actually colourless and the hairs are hollow, so the fur tends to pick up the colouring of its surroundings. Staying camouflaged

in the white surroundings, they hunt seals, crouched motionless by a hole in the ice, sometimes waiting for hours for the seals to pop up. Polar bears have good eyesight and a protective inner eyelid that helps keep the glare of the sun on snow and ice from blinding them. They will use temporary dens for several reasons: as a maternity den, a winter shelter, or as a temporary resting place to escape bad weather. They may stay in the den for a couple of days or for three to four months.

Polar bears stay white all year round.

ARCTIC AMBASSADOR CENTRE

Polar bears are listed as vulnerable and are at risk of becoming critically endangered. Biologists estimate there are only approximately 20,000 to 25,000 polar bears in the wild with approximately 60% of those living in Canada. The Toronto Zoo's breeding program works closely with other zoological associations and conservation institutions, including an important partnership with Polar Bears International (PBI) as an Arctic Ambassador Centre. As such, the Toronto Zoo continues to fulfill our conservation education mission by actively engaging the public in better understanding the impact of climate change on polar bears and their arctic habitat. By working together, the hope is that we can educate the public about climate change, how we can help, and provide leadership for carbon emission reductions in our communities.

One of the key programs under the PBI umbrella is "Acres for the Atmosphere." This is a roll-up-your-sleeves tree-planting and educational effort. Immediate actions are being taken to offset the effects of climate change to help save not only the polar bear, but many other species. Members create carbon sinks by organizing planting events within their communities and carrying out energy conservation campaigns to help reduce carbon emissions. These community events create a group identity that fosters a sense of responsibility for the local environment, and, in turn, promotes respect for the global environment as a whole.

Polar Bears International is a non-profit organization dedicated to the worldwide conservation of the polar bear and its habitat through research, stewardship, and education. They provide scientific resources and information on polar bears and their habitat to institutions and the general public worldwide. The Toronto Zoo is also actively participating in some research that aims to directly help save polar bears in the wild. For more information visit: polarbearsinternational.org

TUNDRA

toronto ZOO

Americas

AMERICAS

TO AFRICAN SAVANNA

DSA

Caribou Café

Polar Patio

TO AUSTRALASIA

*N*orth and South America experience very different climates, stretching a great distance both above and below the equator. There are cold northern and high-altitude regions and vast and highly complex rainforests with incredible biodiversity of plants and animals. Volcanic mountain chains, mangrove swamps, and sandy

Mayan Temple Ruin

Weather Station

Beavertails

General Store

beaches provide habitats for millions of different species. The Americas Pavilion highlights these habitats: rare monkeys, snakes, colourful birds, alligators, marine life, fish, frogs, spiders, beavers, otters, and many more! Outside, visit the South American waterfall and Mayan Temple Ruin to see jaguars, spider monkeys, flamingos, and others.

These beautiful and colourful birds are native to South and Central America.

Scarlet-headed Blackbird
Amblyramphus holosericeus

Blue-crowned Motmot
Momotus momota

toronto ZOO

Two-toed Sloth
Choloepus didactylus

Found widely distributed throughout the rainforests of Central and South America, sloths generally live high in the forest canopy. There are several different species of sloths, including two-toed and three-toed which share similar characteristics.

Most of the sloth's life is spent upside down, including breeding and giving birth. When the female is giving birth, the baby emerges headfirst and pulls itself up onto the mother's belly, thus assisting in its own birth. The two-toed sloth has two digits on the forelimbs and three on the hindlimbs with long, curved claws used to hang from branches and for defence.

Sloths have adapted in many ways to ensure their survival in the rainforest. For example, hanging with all four limbs close together and being greenish-grey, the sloth looks like a bunch of dried leaves. The hairs of their long outer fur have grooves where single-cell algae live, giving the sloth a green sheen and providing further camouflage in the trees.

The slow-moving sloths are still quite common in rainforests, which is surprising when there are so many large birds of prey and tree-climbing carnivores. However, their protective colouration seems to be one of the main factors contributing to the sloth's survival. They also have thick skin and heavy fur and are able to recover from wounds that would be fatal to many other species.

Ancestors of present-day sloths can be traced back about 60 million years. There were tree sloths (all species today are tree sloths) and ground sloths. Some species of ground sloths were the size of elephants.

Boa Constrictor
Constrictor constrictor

The boa constrictor reaches 4 m in length a n d   i s found in the warm climates of Central and South America. Their coloration varies from yellow to black in a complex pattern that acts as camouflage. S p e n d i n g much of their time up in the trees (tropical rainforest or semi-desert regions), they are excellent climbers. Boas give birth to live young, up to 30-50 at a time. Their diet normally consists of large lizards, birds, and small mammals.

> Boas (and pythons) have remnants of limbs in the form of two nail-like spurs on the underside of their tail. Therefore, we know that snakes' ancestors had limbs.

Common Marmoset
Callithrix jacchus

These small monkeys are found leaping through the trees of rainforests in northeastern Brazil. Marmosets travel in groups of about 8–10 individuals. In one day, they may travel 500–1,000 m; thus, they have a large home range (5,000–65,000 sq. m). Their distinctive white ear tufts are present in adults and juveniles. Infants have only grey fur around their neck and head. Marmosets use the trees as their home and also for their food. Their diet consists of insects, fruit, and sap and gum from inside trees. Their teeth are specialized for gnawing holes in trees to extract this sap.

AMERICAS

toronto ZOO

Prehensile-tailed Porcupine
Coendou prehensilis

Prehensile-tailed porcupines are found in eastern South America from eastern Venezuela and Trinidad to northeastern Argentina and Uruguay. Usually found in vine-covered rainforests, but can also be found in farming areas, gardens and drier forests near a water source.

Prehensile-tailed porcupines spend most of their time high in the trees, but since they are unable to leap from tree to tree, they travel from tree to tree on the ground. They normally move rather slowly, but can speed up if necessary. The long, prehensile tail, combined with padded long-clawed toes makes them excellent climbers. The last third of the tail is unspined on its upper surface, providing a smooth contact point for wrapping around even thin branches.

During the day, they sleep in a supportive clump of vegetation in the canopy. At night, they feed on fruits and seeds as well as stems, leaves, roots and bark. When threatened by a predator, they sometimes roll into a ball with quills raised, and will occasionally lunge at an attacker with spines erect.

Golden Lion Tamarin
Leontopithecus rosalia

The golden lion tamarin is one of the world's most critically endangered mammals, mostly because of rainforest destruction in southeastern Brazil, which results in loss of habitat. More than 90 percent of their Atlantic coastal forest habitat has been lost or fragmented to obtain lumber and charcoal and to clear out areas for plantations, cattle pastures, and development. Their fur is silky and golden coloured with a characteristic mane that surrounds their bare face. Tamarins are agile in their forested habitat and are able to leap from tree to tree with ease.

White-faced Saki Monkey
Pithecia pithecia

Another South American monkey, sakis are active tree-dwellers that rarely come to the ground. They have excellent jumping ability and can cover 10 m in a single leap when escaping danger. Only the males have white faces; females have dark faces with pale stripes along the sides of the nose. They live in groups and defend their territory with loud calls and aggressive body movements.

Tiger Rat Snake
Spilotes pullatus

One of the longer and most beautiful snakes in the Americas is the tiger rat snake. It is brilliantly coloured with yellow, black, white, and orange markings. This pattern provides camouflage for them in the forested areas they inhabit, where the sun shines through the trees. They are able to move quickly through the forest in pursuit of prey. They also have enlarged eyes, giving them excellent eyesight and improving their hunting skills. Tiger rat snakes eat small mammals, lizards, frogs, other snakes, and birds.

AMERICAS

toronto ZOO

Americas Fishes and Marine Invertebrates

The marine invertebrates found in the Americas section of the Zoo are adapted to a temperate, marine environment (10°C). Surprising to some, these species are native to Canada, as well as coastal USA. Their environment is constantly changing: twelve-hour tide cycles mean they are alternately subjected to open air and sunlight or submerged in chilling waters and rushing waves. Comparatively, the Great Barrier Reef exhibit in the Australasia pavilion is an example of a warm and tropical marine environment.

Giant Pacific Octopus
Enteroctopus dolleini

This is the largest octopus and it is found in the cold waters of the Pacific Ocean from California north to Alaska. They inhabit natural den and cave-like areas on the ocean floor. Octopuses have some unusual and fascinating adaptations to ensure survival in the ocean: their skin can change colour to blend with the background, and they have excellent sight, smell, and taste. The octopus lacks a skeleton, enabling it to squeeze into a variety of small spaces for protection. Also, it has the ability to squirt "ink," which acts as a smokescreen, allowing it to escape from predators. The octopus stalks its prey and uses its tentacles to trap the prey within their grasp. It has a parrot-like beak, which pierces the crustacean's shell and injects toxins which kill the prey.

With eight (octo) arms and over 2,000 suckers on its tentacles, an octopus can hold down prey that is ten times its weight; humans can usually support only two times their weight.

Pink Star
Pisaster brevispinus

Starfish are invertebrates with a symmetrical 5-part body plan. Tiny rows of tube feet on the underside of its arms act as suction discs, and are used for locomotion and also to grasp food, passing it to the central mouth. The tube feet are also breathing organs. They eat sponges, coral, worms, molluscs, and crustaceans. To eat these creatures, the starfish turns its stomach inside out and extrudes it through a tiny hole. The stomach is a transparent bag that it wraps around the prey, completely surrounding it for digestion. If the prey has a shell (e.g., a mussel), the starfish attaches its suctioning tube feet to the shell and pulls it apart.

Green Surf Anemone
Anthopleura xanthogrammica

Sea anemones are found in many different sizes and beautiful colours. They look like plants but are actually carnivorous animals, related to jellyfish. The anemone is column-shaped with tentacles on top; the stomach is inside the column. As a fish swims by, it is drawn to the tentacles of the anemone, which sting and paralyze it, and draw the food to the anemone's mouth. The base of the anemone forms a smooth, slippery disc that allows it to slide about or hold onto rocks. Anemones reproduce in several ways: by splitting into two; by cloning from pieces of the base that get left behind when the anemone travels; or by releasing eggs and sperm into the water — the fertilized egg develops into a free-swimming larva that moves away to new territory and changes into an adult and eventually settles down.

Anemones range in size from a few millimetres to 1.5 metres in diameter!

Cardinal Tetra
Paracheirodon axelrodi

The cardinal tetra is a small, brightly coloured schooling fish that is popular in the aquarium trade. They are bright red with a vivid blue stripe across the middle of their body. Most of these fish have teeth, some only in the upper jaw. They feed on plankton, worms, and small crustaceans. Adults are about 5 cm long; females are usually a little larger and have larger stomachs than the males. They are found in South America from Brazil to Colombia and Venezuela. They prefer slow-moving waters, generally living near the bottom where it is dark.

Conservation: Project Piaba: More than 20 million ornamental fishes are harvested from the Amazon region. Project Piaba works with local communities by promoting responsible fishing practices and locating overseas markets. By conserving the fishery the surrounding forest, rivers and streams are also protected.

toronto ZOO

Red-breasted Piranha
Pyocentrus nattereri

Piranhas are not very large but they can swim fast and have sharp teeth, thus making them dangerous predators in the water. Found in parts of Central, and South America, piranhas inhabit rivers and streams. These carnivorous fish feed mostly on small fish, birds and frogs, but will also attack small mammals.

Like most fish, piranhas have an acute sense of smell that helps them to detect the location of their prey. Their head is short and compressed, supported by strong muscles, and their powerful interlocking teeth are razor sharp. Their tail section, which is slender and muscular, and their blade-shaped tail fin enable them to move rapidly through the water towards their prey. They live in schools and biologists believe there are up to 35 different species of piranhas.

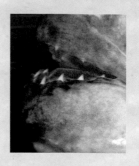

Blue Poison Dart Frog
Dendrobates azureus

These South American frogs are both blue and poisonous, as their name suggests. Glands in their skin secrete a highly toxic poison. They are named dart frogs because their poison has been used by some tribes to tip hunting darts. Living in the dark and moist tropical rainforests, dart frogs are land dwellers but always stay close to a water source. They feed on small insects, termites, and ants. Similar to other brightly coloured animals, their bright blue skin acts as a warning to predators not to approach them. *Visit our frog dome to see more species of poison dart frogs.*

The poison they secrete is a product of their diet; therefore, the poison is not present in animals in captivity.

Axolotl
Ambystoma mexicanum

Axolotls are amphibians that spend their entire life in the water. This critically endangered species is found only in Lake Xochimilco in southeast Mexico City. Axolotls exist as sexually mature larvae, never metamorphosing out of this stage (compared to frogs that metamorphose from a tadpole to a frog). As embryos, they develop inside eggs and then transform into larvae. After two weeks, the larva develops small feathery gills, front legs, and a long tail. Two weeks later it develops hind legs. Using their gills, they breathe mostly underwater but sometimes supplement this by going to the water surface and taking quick breaths of air.

 Conservation: The axolotl population is declining because of large amounts of pollution in the lake and the introduction of exotic species. The Toronto Zoo is working with agencies and community groups in Mexico City on habitat restoration and conservation education.

Eyelash Viper
Bothriechis schleglii

This nocturnal snake is one of the smallest snakes (50–80 cm) in Central America. Eyelash vipers are almost completely arboreal (tree dwelling) and have strong tails for supporting them when wrapped around a branch. To feed, they hold onto a branch with their tails and strike with great speed to catch and eat their food (small mammals, lizards, frogs, and birds). Eyelash vipers are beautifully coloured from green to yellow. These bright colours help them to camouflage among the tropical rainforest flowers. They tend to hide in the flowers where their prey is also found. Their "eyelashes" (enlarged scales above their eyes) also help them to blend in with the surrounding foliage.

They have two fangs in the front of their mouth that fold back when their mouth is closed.

toronto ZOO

Black-footed Ferret
Mustela nigripes

Black-footed ferrets are highly specialized predators from the weasel family. They have long, slender bodies that give them great flexibility to maneuver in tight burrows. They also have strong jaws and very sharp teeth. These nocturnal hunters feed almost exclusively on the black-tailed prairie dog, and this dependence is the main reason for their decline.

Black-footed ferrets historically ranged in the North American prairies, from southern Canada to northern Mexico. However, as humans converted prairie to pastureland, farmers did their best to rid their land

of prairie dogs. Thousands of prairie dogs were poisoned and with the crash of prairie dog populations came the plight of the black-footed ferret. In less than a century this once wide-ranging species became restricted to only a few isolated areas in the United States. In 1979, the last known wild ferret died. The black-footed ferret was considered extinct.

Two years later a miracle occurred. A black-footed ferret was spotted on a farm in Wyoming. Researchers fled to the area and discovered a living population of ferrets. Over the next few years, ferrets from this population were captured and used to start a captive breeding program. Since then, thousands of black-footed ferret kits have been born in captivity and hundreds released to sites throughout the ferret's historical range. Toronto Zoo is the only facility in Canada breeding black-footed ferrets for reintroduction. Our proudest moment came in 2009 when ferrets were released into Grasslands National Park, Saskatchewan. This marked the first time in over 70 years that wild ferrets roamed free in Canada.

Today, over a thousand black-footed ferrets live in the wild but they still need our help. As always, the survival of ferrets depends on the survival of prairie dogs. Diseases such as canine distemper virus and sylvatic plague threaten ferret and prairie dog populations alike. To combat these diseases, veterinarians from the Toronto Zoo now travel to Grasslands National Park regularly to administer vaccines to wild ferrets and their newborn kits.

CONSERVATION AND RECOVERY PROGRAM

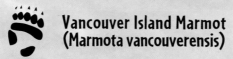

Vancouver Island Marmot
(Marmota vancouverensis)

As its name suggests, the Vancouver Island marmot can be found only on Vancouver Island in British Columbia. One of the rarest mammals in the world, this species is classified as Endangered under Canada's Species at Risk Act and by the Committee on the Status of Endangered Wildlife in Canada. As well, they are considered Critically Endangered by the International Union for the Conservation of Nature.

Vancouver Island marmots have a very restricted range, inhabiting alpine meadows between 900 and 1,500 m above sea level. Marmot populations experienced significant declines during the 1990s, mainly due to high predation rates by wolves, cougars and golden eagles. By 2003 there were less than 30 individuals left in the wild.

Fortunately, the Government of British Columbia had the foresight to organize a Vancouver Island Marmot Recovery Team whose task was to determine how to save the species from extinction. From 1997-2004, 56 wild marmots were captured and became founders of today's captive breeding and release program. Currently, there are four institutions involved in the captive breeding program: Toronto Zoo, Calgary Zoo, Mountain View Conservation Society and the Tony Barrett Mount Washington Marmot Breeding Centre. Captive breeding has been very successful at the Toronto Zoo and over 100 pups have been born here since the start of the program.

In 2003, as the wild population reached its critical point, the first captive-bred marmots were released on Vancouver Island. Annual reintroductions have continued and many marmots now survive their first hibernation period, the biggest test for wild marmots. Vancouver Island marmot populations have made an amazing recovery due to the efforts of the Recovery Team. Today, the wild population contains hundreds of animals and marmots are now living and reproducing on mountains from which they had previously disappeared.

toronto ZOO

AMERICAS

AMPHIBIAN BREEDING CENTRE
AMPHIBIAN CONSERVATION

After more than 360 million years of survival, 1/3 to 1/2 of the world's approximately 6,000 known amphibian species could become extinct in our lifetime. Earth is facing the single largest mass extinction since the disappearance of dinosaurs. Many of these amphibian species are threatened by disease.

With your support, the Toronto Zoo is helping to rescue frogs and other amphibians as part of a global conservation initiative. Our staff use their expertise to establish and breed assurance populations so these species do not disappear forever.

Puerto Rican Crested Toad
Bufo lemur

The Puerto Rican crested toad is the only toad native to Puerto Rico and it occurs in semi-arid to arid habitats where it lives in Karst limestone formations. The toad populations once existed as two distinct populations; one in the north and the other in the south. Significant differences in the mitochondrial DNA suggest that the two populations have been separated for over 1 million years. Unfortunately, the northern toads have not been seen in the wild since 1988 and are considered extirpated. The only known wild population is the southern form, which occurs in Guanica National Forest. They breed in seasonal pools formed after hurricanes or tropical storms. Tadpoles develop in 18 days and leave the ponds before they dry up. The Toronto Zoo has returned over 100,000 tadpoles back to the wild and constructed ponds for their release. Tadpoles bred at Toronto Zoo and returned to Puerto Rico are now adults and breeding in ponds constructed for their release. We collaborate with many zoos in the United States and Puerto Rico as well as the U.S. Fish and Wildlife Service and Department of Natural Resources to help Puerto Ricans preserve this unique species.

Golden Harlequin Frog
Atelopus varius

The golden harlequin frog, also known as the Panamanian golden frog, is found only on the mountain slopes of western Panama. Like most colourful frogs, the golden harlequin frog contains poisonous chemicals in its skin. Its extremely bright colouration warns predators that it is toxic. They feed on insects and other small invertebrates. They live along streams in moist tropical woodland habitat and breed in temporary pools and small ponds. While most frogs are known for their vocalizations, this species prefers hand-waving, which is used to attract mates and settle territorial disputes. This behaviour, known as semaphoring, is probably an adaptation to the noisiness of their environment (streams) and takes advantage of their keen eyesight. The Toronto Zoo has partnered with Project Golden Frog to help rescue some of the world's rarest frogs, including

the golden harlequin frog. This species has declined due to the loss of most of its natural habitat to logging and conversion into cultivated pasture and urbanized land-uses. It is also suffering from the effects of a pathogenic chytrid fungus, which was discovered, in 1998, to be threatening

numerous species of frogs in many parts of the world.

Cuvier's Smooth-fronted Caiman
Paleosuchus palpebrosus

Cuvier's smooth-fronted caiman, also called the dwarf caiman, is one of the smallest of the crocodilians, averaging 1.2–1.5 m in length. Found mainly within the Amazon and Orinoco river basins in South America, they tend to stay in areas with fast-moving rapids and deeply shaded waterfalls. They spend most of the day in the water and rarely bask in the sun. Dwarf caimans can sense movement at a fair distance, which allows them to catch fast-moving prey. Their prey includes small fish, amphibians, snails, crustaceans, birds, and mammals. The female builds a mound from soil and vegetation above the water in which to lay her eggs. Incubation is approximately three months long.

> When the baby caimans are ready to hatch, they will scratch at the shell of their egg, notifying their mother that they're ready to come out!

toronto ZOO

North American River Otter
Lutra canadensis canadensis

River otters always seem to be having a lot of fun. These highly social animals enjoy playing, swimming, and sliding around. When a young otter is born, its eyes are closed and stay closed for about 35 days. At about 5–6 weeks old, otters begin to play, and at 10–12 weeks, the mother teaches them to swim and hunt. The otter is nearly full-grown at one year of age. It can stay submerged for two minutes or more, allowing it to swim under ice to another open hole. They swim using mostly their body and tail, only paddling a little with their hind feet. The river otter lives in dens located in banks along a stream or lake. The den may have just a few simple tunnels or contain a complex tunnel system. Materials used to line the dens are dry wood chips, leaves, and bark.

Black Widow Spider
Latrodectus

Found worldwide in drier habitats, the black widow got its name because it was believed the female killed the male after mating; however, this is generally not the case. Black widow males will often mate a second time. The female is glossy black with a red hourglass

shape on the underside of her abdomen. The male also has this hourglass mark, but is smaller and paler in colour. The female spins a soft silk cocoon in which to lay her eggs. She then wraps a second layer of stronger silk and, lastly, a third layer of waterproof silk around the egg case. As a true spider, the black widow's fangs move from side to side, horizontally (tarantulas' fangs move up and down).

The black widow spider does not aggressively hunt humans. When they bite it is to defend themselves or their eggs.

TURTLES OF THE AMAZON

Mata Mata
Chelus fimbriatus

The mata mata is a very large, flat turtle found in the Amazon, well camouflaged to mimic the leaves on pond bottoms of flooded forests or slow moving streams. When the turtle quickly opens its mouth, unwary fish are captured in the stream of rushing water. This turtle is known as a side-necked turtle. Unlike your typical turtle --you know the ones that pull their heads straight back to hide in their shell, these turtles simply bend their long necks sideways and tuck their head under the lip of their shell.

Another side-necked turtle is the yellow-spotted river turtle (*Podocnemis unifilis*). This species is one of the largest South American river turtles found throughout the Orinoco and Amazon River basins. During the high-water period, they are also found in flooded forests, swamps and lagoons. They feed primarily on vegetation and some fruit, and are an important agent in the distribution of seeds which germinate after passing through the turtle's digestive system. The yellow-spotted river turtle gets its name from yellow spots which remain present in males throughout life.

AMERICAS

toronto ZOO

American Alligator
Alligator mississippiensis

These alligators are found in the southern United States. Food consists of anything from fish and frogs to turtles, snakes, rodents and other small mammals. Alligators play an important role in keeping populations of rodents, such as the muskrat, under control. They also construct "gator holes" in drying wetlands. These depressions, created by alligators, provide water for many other wetland species during periods of drought. The male American alligator can measure as long as 3 m; females are generally about 2 m long. The alligator's jaw is hinged on the bottom and fixed on the top. Each jaw contains 40 teeth; which are constantly replaced throughout the alligator's life; the upper set of teeth lies outside the lower set when the mouth is closed. One of the first species protected in the U.S., the alligator's population recovery is a conservation success story.

Spiny Softshelled Turtle
Apalone spinifera spinifera

Spiny softshelled turtles were once found in several areas of southern Ontario and southern Quebec; however, they are now rare in both areas. The distinguishing feature of these turtles is their soft shell — most turtles have hard shells. They live in rivers, lakes or swamps where there is a sandy or muddy bottom and some aquatic vegetation. They also inhabit areas near sandy or gravelly shoreline where they can nest. Females usually lay about 12–18 eggs per year. During the winter months, spiny softshelled turtles hibernate underwater in sand or mud. Many factors have contributed to their decline in numbers. Their nesting and hibernating areas are being fragmented or completely lost due to construction on shorelines. Chemical pollution and sewage are contaminating their waters. They are also affected by human disturbance during nesting times, fluctuating water levels, and heavy predation of the eggs by raccoons, foxes, and other animals.

 Conservation: Toronto Zoo is a member of the recovery teams for all turtle species at risk in Ontario.

Gila Monster
Heloderma suspectum suspectum

Mexican Beaded Lizard
Heloderma horridum

Gila monsters, along with Mexican beaded lizards, are the world's only venomous lizards. Found in the southern United States and Mexico, Gila monsters are smaller in size than the Mexican beaded lizard. Gila monsters tend to favour semi-arid regions at the foothills of mountain ranges. As opportunistic foragers, they actively hunt and seek available foods. They detect and identify prey by chemical cues and odours picked up by their constantly flicking snake-like tongues. They feed on a variety of prey such as desert squirrels, young rodents, and the eggs of quails, tortoises, and other reptiles. During the breeding season, when the male encounters a female, a wonderful courtship ritual begins of chin-rubbing and nose-nudging. The gestation period is about 45 days resulting in a clutch of 2–12 eggs (averaging five).

San Esteban Island Chuckwalla
Sauromalus varius

Found on San Esteban Island in the Sea of Cortés, this is the largest of the five species of chuckwallas reaching 76 cm in overall length and weighing up to 1.4 kg. It is considered a textbook example of island gigantism as it is 3 to 4 times the size of its mainland counterparts. It is also the most endangered of all the chuckwallas. It feeds on a variety of flowers, leaves, cactus fruits, berries and insects. When threatened, chuckwallas will retreat into a rock crevice and inflate its body, thus wedging itself into their retreat.

Desert Grassland Whiptail
Cnemidophorus uniparens

Life Without Males?

This beautiful and active lizard is found in the desert grasslands and semi-desert grasslands of Arizona, New Mexico, Texas and various locations in Mexico. This is an all-female species and there is no sexual reproduction since the eggs are not fertilized. The young are essentially clones of their mother. They are most active in the early morning and late afternoon, and feed on a variety of insects, including ants and termites, as well as insect larvae.

AMERICAS

toronto ZOO

Pacific Rattlesnake
Crotalus oreganus

Only four populations of this threatened species are found in the interior of British Columbia. This snake often hibernates communally and this makes them particularly vulnerable to persecution by people.

Conservation: Toronto Zoo supports conservation programs for this species including education programs developed by the Nk'Mip Desert and Heritage Centre and the Osoyoos Indian Band.

Canadian Beaver
Castor canadensis

Familiar to Canadians, the beaver is found throughout North America, excluding the extreme north. Their forefeet have five digits that function as fingers, but their hind feet are webbed, which aids swimming. To groom their fur, they use a double claw on the second hind toe as a comb. Each jaw has two incisors that never stop growing and must be worn down constantly, as well as, four rootless molars. Famous for felling trees, beavers use their upper incisors to cut a ring around the trunk. Secondly, they sink their lower incisors into the trunk below the ring and lever out a large chip. From there they work above and below the ring to cause the tree to fall. Two beavers working in shifts can cut down an aspen 25 cm in diameter in four hours. Young beaver kits can swim a few hours after birth and live with the colony for two years before being forced out to find their own territory. All members of the family help gather materials to build their lodge, which is generally 2.5–3.5 m in diameter and 1 m high.

The beaver is the largest rodent in North America.

Butterfly Goodeid
Ameca splendens

The butterfly goodeid was formerly found in the Ameca River drainage in Mexico within an area about 15 km in diameter. It was thought to be extinct in the wild, but a remnant population has been found to persist in El Rincón waterpark near the town of Ameca. It may also exist in a feral state in the USA due to escaped or introduced captive stock. They give birth to live young. Fertilization is via an internal oviduct with a placenta-like organ that allows them to give birth to fully developed young. Frequently fry are born with the umbilical cord still attached, which disappears in 2 to 3 days. They feed on live worms or aquatic animals that will fit into its small mouth. They like to browse on water plants, green hair algae or blue-green algae. They may also eat duckweed.

Blind Cave Characin
Astyanax jordani

Blind cave characins are found in underground rivers and lakes in caves from Texas to Mexico. They are troglobites (a species that is confined to caves and live in constant darkness). As a result, these fish have vestigial (non-functioning) eyes which are covered over by layers of skin. The larvae have normal eyes when they hatch, but these become enclosed in tissue after a few weeks. With no functioning eyes, they depend on their lateral lines to detect motion in the water for finding food, as well as locating enemies and avoiding obstacles. They also have a very good sense of smell. These fish have teeth set in their jaws with a replacement row behind the functional row. Their skin is smooth and lacks pigmentation, giving it a pinkish hue. They are omnivorous – feeding on plants, invertebrates, and other fish.

Capybara
Hydrochoerus hydrochaeris

The name capybara means "water pig" in Greek. They are found in Panama, Colombia, Venezuela, Peru, Brazil, Paraguay, northeast Argentina, and Uruguay. They prefer flooded grasslands, but are also found in various wetlands. They feed primarily on grasses and aquatic plants. They are known as a "keystone species" because they are the largest grazers in their habitats and dramatically change it as they move from place to place, which other species rely on for survival. Capybaras are highly social and live in groups of around 20 individuals, with a dominant male. Capybaras communicate using both scent (secreted by glands) and sound.

AMERICAS

Capybaras are the world's largest living rodent weighing approximately 45 kg (100 lbs).

Tarantulas

Tarantulas mainly feed on insects and other arthropods but bigger ones can also ambush lizards, mice, birds and small snakes. All tarantulas are venomous but are harmless to humans. The popularity in the pet trade has led to the discovery of many new species.

toronto **ZOO**

American Eel
Anguilla rostrata

American eels are found in coastal, fresh and marine waters from Greenland to South America. They undergo an extraordinary migration from the Sargasso Sea in the Atlantic Ocean, which is the only place in the world  that they spawn. Once the eggs hatch, the larvae (leptocephalus) are carried by the Gulf Stream. Near the coast, they change into glass eels and migrate inland into streams, rivers and lakes to grow and become elvers. Three to 12 months later they become yellow eels, but it will be 10 to 25 years before they become adult silver eels and ready to make their long trip back to the Sargasso Sea to spawn and repeat the whole cycle again.

Eastern Massasauga Rattlesnake
Sistrurus catenatus catenatus

 Found in southern Ontario and nine northeastern U.S. states, this medium-size rattlesnake can grow up to 1 m long. At birth, the young average about 22 cm in length. The rattle, composed of modified scales, grows in length as the snake grows. In young snakes the rattle starts off as a "button," and each time the skin is shed (about 3–4 times a year), a new segment is added. As an adult, the rattle is a fully formed organ of loosely attached interlocking segments that strike against each other to produce a buzzing sound when the tail is vibrated rapidly. They also possess fangs that inject venom into their prey. Massasauga rattlesnakes are a threatened species, largely due to habitat loss and persecution by humans out of fear.

 The Toronto Zoo is working to help people learn to live with rattlesnakes and inform them on how to protect this species. To attend a rattlesnake workshop or for more information email aap@torontozoo.ca

WETLAND TURTLES

Wetlands created by beavers benefit many species including turtles and amphibians. Six of eight Ontario turtles are threatened and two are at risk of extinction. As part of the Urban Turtle initiative, Toronto Zoo is studying turtles in the Toronto area including the Rouge Valley.

 Get involved: Ontario Frogwatch and Ontario Turtle Tally are programs that provide opportunities to monitor wetlands. Send sightings of frogs and turtles to the Adopt-A-Pond Wetlands Conservation Program at torontozoo.com/AdoptAPond/

Snapping Turtle
Chelydra serpentina

The snapping turtle is the largest freshwater turtle in Canada. It can weigh up to 35 kg with a carapace length of up to 40 cm. The shell of the snapping turtle is rough, but becomes smooth with age. The plastron (lower shell) is cross-shaped and very small. For this reason, the turtle cannot tuck its head and limbs fully inside its protective shell – hence its pugnacious reputation when disturbed on land. However, we have nothing to fear when in the water, as snapping turtles simply swim away from any disturbance! They prefer slow moving water with a soft muddy bottom and plenty of aquatic vegetation or submerged brush and tree trunks for cover. They feed on fish, frogs, insects, crustaceans and any other small animal they can catch.

MAYAN TEMPLE RUIN
(OUTDOOR EXHIBITS)

American Flamingo
Phoenicopterus ruber ruber

Although females are generally smaller than males, flamingos can grow to be 1.7 m tall. The Zoo's flamingos stay together in a group the same way they would in the wild, except the flock would number in the thousands. They live in salt lakes and lagoons on the Atlantic coast of Central and South America. Nests for the flamingo's eggs are usually built in shallow water or in open expanses of mud. The nests are made of mud that the flamingo rakes up with its bill, shaping it into a cone and creating a shallow depression on top. Usually, one egg is laid and is incubated by both the male and the female for 30–32 days. The flamingo's famous pink colour is due to its diet. The carotene in the shrimp it feeds on turns its feathers pink. If their diet is lacking or low in carotene, the feathers will become white.

Flamingo parents are able to recognize their own chicks, even when they are among a dense crowd of other flamingo chicks.

toronto ZOO

Black-handed Spider Monkey
Ateles geoffroyi geoffroyi

Of all the primates, the spider monkey has the most mobile and dextrous prehensile (the ability to grasp) tail. At the Zoo, you'll see them swinging from ropes and trees, using their arms and legs as well as their tails. The last 25 cm of the tail is covered with finely ridged skin that helps provide a grip and is as sensitive as skin on the hand. The tail alone can support the full weight of the animal. Their legs and tail are very long in proportion to the body length; the body is 38–64 cm long and the tail is 51–89 cm long. The spider monkey has hook-like hands that help it swing fast through the trees; their thumbs are very small.

Black-handed spider monkeys have one of the most highly developed larynxes of all the monkeys, which gives them a wide range of vocalizations – from bird calls to barking to grunting.

Jaguar
Panthera onca

The jaguar is an extremely powerful animal and the largest cat in the Americas. It is recognized by its short massive legs, broad head, and characteristic rosettes (spots). The jaguars that are melanistic (all black) have spots, but they can be seen only in certain lighting. As long as 1.2–1.8 m, jaguars can weigh between 90–120 kg for males and 60–90 kg for females. Adding to their power, jaguars are strong swimmers and excellent climbers, enabling them to follow their prey and chase them through water or trees. Generally, jaguars are solitary animals except during courtship or mating or when the mother has cubs. The female jaguar has her cubs in a den after a gestation of about 93–105 days. By the age of two, the cubs are ready to hunt on their own and leave their family to find their own territory and mate.

A jaguar's jaw is said to be the second strongest of any land mammal, strong enough to crush a turtle shell. The hyena has the strongest jaw.

HORTICULTURE AT THE ZOO

The Toronto Zoo occupies 287 hectares, including a 165-hectare valley and wooded area that are conserved in their natural state. The Horticulture staff plans and develops the indoor and outdoor exhibits, and manages the landscaping and natural areas.

Americas Plants

Powderpuff
Calliandra haematocephala,
Mimosa Family, Mimosaceae

Found in tropical regions, the flower cluster of this plant resembles a powderpuff. Numerous long stamens give the flower its characteristic appearance. The flower is also a source of nectar for hummingbirds.

Bromeliad Family, Bromeliaceae

Native to South and Central America, this plant Family includes the pineapple and spanish moss. In most species snug-fitting leaves collect pools of water that provide a complete habitat for small animals and a water source for tree-top animals. Bromeliads are epiphytes: plants that live above the ground by growing on other plants or other supports. Bromeliads are not parasites. They make their own food from sunlight and water.

Lobster Claw
Heliconia rostrata,
Heliconia Family, Heliconiaceae

This stunning plant has dark green leaves and bright red and yellow bracts (modified leaves) surrounding the flower. Found in tropical regions of South America, the pendulous blooms may reach 1 m in length.

Walking Iris
Neomarica gracilis, Iris Family, Iridacae

Walking iris is a herbaceous plant (soft-stemmed plant) with sword-shaped leaves arranged in a fan. The fleur-de-lis flower is purple and white. After the flower fades, the stem falls to the ground and takes root some distance from the original plant, hence the name "walking iris."

toronto ZOO

Australasia

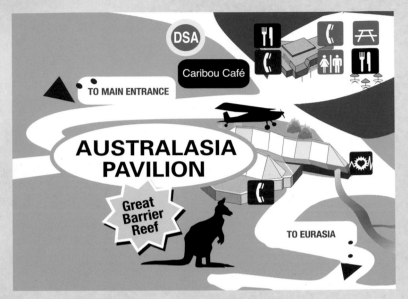

*A*ustralia is a spectacular and varied land mass. Generally warm throughout, Australia ranges from a flat, dry, and barren interior to a fertile and humid east coast, home of the Great Barrier Reef. Australia is known for many of its own surprising and unique animals and plants. Australia and the islands north of it make up the zoogeographic region of Australasia. Discover some of Australia's unique species, such as kangaroos, echidnas, wombats, kookaburras, and wallabies in the Australasia Pavilion. The pavilion is also home to the world's largest lizard, the Komodo dragon, seahorses, Great Barrier Reef fishes, moon jellies, turtles, snakes, and lizards. Outside is the exciting Aussie walkabout, where you can walk among a mob of kangaroos, wallabies, and emus.

White's Tree Frog
Litoria caerulea

Also known as the Australian green tree frog, this species has a bluish green to emerald green back which can change shades depending on the temperature of the environment. The fatty ridge over the eye is a very distinct trait of this species. Males are smaller than females which can average 10 cm long. Native to Australia, Indonesia and Papua New Guinea, these frogs are found in a range of habitats, typically in the canopy of trees near a water source or wherever there is high humidity and cooler temperatures. Large discs on their fingers and toes enable this frog to climb in search of water or damp places to live during dry periods and they may climb building walls where they catch flying insects attracted to lights. This adaptability allows it to share suburban and urban areas with humans. However, one of the main threats to this species is habitat loss associated with urban expansion, particularly in the coastal areas. Chytrid fungus has also been found to be impacting their survival with concern of a widespread epidemic in the near future.

AUSTRALASIA

toronto ZOO

Matschie's Tree Kangaroo
Dendrolagus matschiei

As you enter the Australasia pavilion, you will notice a curious animal, most likely up in the trees. The Matschie's tree kangaroo is the most brilliantly coloured of marsupials. The length of the body is 52–81 cm, and the tail is long and furry, providing a balancing device. Thick fur on the back of the neck grows in reverse direction, acting as a water-shedding device as the animal generally sits with its head lower than its shoulders. They are very agile in trees and can leap as far as 9 m downward to an adjoining tree. Most of their day is spent in trees; however, they are able to jump to the ground from remarkable heights without injury. They live in inaccessible areas in the Huon Peninsula, Papua New Guinea; therefore, their numbers and habitat are not well known but they are considered threatened due to habitat loss and hunting.

Victoria Crowned Pigeon
Goura victoria

As you walk through the Australasia pavilion you will notice many birds but only one bears a crown! Although Victoria crowned pigeons may be difficult to see hiding among trees and plants, they are social birds who usually live in a group with 5 to 15 others. They grow to be about the size of a large chicken with a small head and red eyes. Their legs are long, as opposed to our native pigeons. The crown is fan-shaped with white tips and can be manipulated by the bird, taking on the look of lace when fully erect. When young pigeons are hatched, the male and female share nesting and feeding duties. The young are fed pigeons' milk, a curd-like material secreted by special cells, and then progress to partially digested food from the parents. Like all pigeons, they drink by sucking up water instead of tilting their heads back to swallow.

Victoria crowned pigeons belong to the same order as the extinct dodo bird.

Solomon Island Leaf Frog
Ceratobatrachus guentheri

Solomon Island leaf frogs are found in Papua New Guinea and Solomon Islands. Its natural habitats are subtropical or tropical moist lowland forests, rural gardens, urban areas, and heavily degraded former forests. This species has many different colour forms within the species. While most frogs lay eggs in the water with an aquatic tadpole stage, this species hatches out of pea-sized eggs as fully developed baby frogs. The eggs are laid in shallow nests dug into the forest floor and the clear outer gel reveals the developing frog inside. They have a noisy call, something like the barking of a small dog.

Kookaburra
Dacelo novaeguineae novaeguineae

The kookaburra, the largest of the kingfishers, has a distinctive broad eyebrow that starts above its beak and tapers off behind the crown. They feed on small mammals, reptiles, frogs and insects. The kookaburra hen nests in hollow trees or tree stumps and lays 3–4 white eggs. Kookaburras will spend a long time on a perch, scanning the ground for prey. After catching its prey, a young bird holds on to one end of it while the adult pulls backwards on the other end until the body of the victim snaps and is torn apart. The young may stay with the family for several years, helping to raise and protect new young. Kookaburras can live for 20 years or more.

The kookaburra has long been known for its "laugh" that is actually a call used to declare its rights over a territory and nest.

toronto ZOO

Live Coral

Worldwide, there are 4,000 different coral species. Coral polyps are tiny soft-bodied invertebrates that are essentially a sac with a single mouth at the top surrounded by tentacles that are used to capture food, such as plankton, with the aid of nematocysts, which are microscopic stinging capsules. The mouth leads into a short tube which opens into the body cavity where digestion and absorption of the food takes place. Coral polyps build the reef by depositing calcium and other minerals absorbed from the salt water and live in massive colonies built on the skeletons of old colonies. Hundreds of thousands of coral polpys make up a coral reef. Natural pigments in coral tissues produce a range of colours, including white, red, orange, yellow, green, blue, and purple. The different shapes represent adaptations to different environmental conditions. Coral that is smooth

Tentacles
Embedded in the tentacles are stinging cells called nematocysts, used to capture floating food. These harpoon-like cells are common to jellyfish, anemones and corals.

Mouth

Hollow thread
Barbs
Trigger
Discharged nematocyst or stinging cell

Polyp

Stomach

Limestone Base

and rounded grows in places where there is strong wave action. Branched coral generally grows in calmer, deeper water.

> Coral reefs are the largest structures created by any animal in the world.

Jellyfish

Jellyfish are actually not fish, but an invertebrate that is related to corals and sea anemones. They inhabit every major oceanic area of the world, even some fresh-water lakes, and have been drifting through the world's oceans for more than

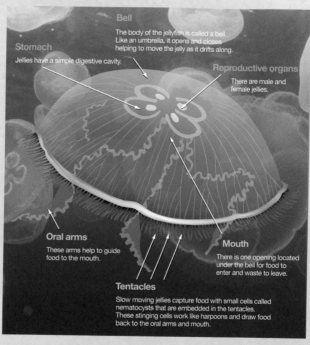

Bell
The body of the jellyfish is called a bell. Like an umbrella, it opens and closes helping to move the jelly as it drifts along.

Stomach
Jellies have a simple digestive cavity.

Reproductive organs
There are male and female jellies.

Oral arms
These arms help to guide food to the mouth.

Mouth
There is one opening located under the bell for food to enter and waste to leave.

Tentacles
Slow moving jellies capture food with small cells called nematocysts that are embedded in the tentacles. These stinging cells work like harpoons and draw food back to the oral arms and mouth.

650 millions years. It is estimated that there may be as many as 2,000 species of jellyfish. They range in size from about 2.5 cm to 61 metres long. They are composed of 97% water and therefore are very fragile. Jellyfish are carnivorous, feeding mostly on a variety of zooplankton.

Moon Jellies
Aurelia aurita

Moon jellies are named for their ghostly, translucent bells. They are found in temperate and tropical waters worldwide. They feed on small plankton, fish eggs and other small jellies. They can reach a size of up to 38 cm in diameter.

toronto ZOO

Great Barrier Reef Community Tank

The Great Barrier Reef community tank is over 7 m in lengh and 32,000 litres in capacity. This tank holds over 1,000 reef fish found in the Great Barrier Reef such as the brown-banded bamboo shark, parrotfish, anglefish, butterflyfish and more, all set within a beautiful coral reef display.

The Great Barrier Reef is the largest natural feature on earth and stretches for more than 2,000 km along the northeast coast of Australia. It is the only living thing on earth that can be seen from space. There are more different species of animals and plants in a cubic metre of the Great Barrier Reef than any other environment in the world, including tropical rainforests.

Lionfish
Pterois volitans

The lionfish is a venomous coral reef fish from the Great Barrier Reef. They can grow up to 43 cm in length. For the majority of their adult life they are solitary and will fiercely defend their home range against intruders using their poisonous dorsal spines. Lionfish are mostly nocturnal and hide in caves and crevices during the day. They feed on crustaceans, as well as other invertebrates, and small fishes. The lionfish herds small fish into corners by extending their expansive fins, then with one swift gulping motion sucks the prey into its mouth. They have little to fear, with their needle sharp spines they are able to deliver a lethal dose of venom to a predator.

Seahorse
Hippocampus sp.

Seahorses are named for their horse-shaped head and upright body position. Although they are bony fish, they do not have scales, but instead have a thin skin stretched over bony rings. Seahorses have prehensile tails, which they use to anchor themselves around seagrass stems, coral heads or other suitable objects. They spend most of their time this way, camouflaged in the grasses and corals, hiding from predators. Seahorses have neither teeth nor stomachs so they must use their tube-shaped snout like a vaccuum to suck up food. Seahorses eat small shrimp, tiny fish and plankton. Their eyes can move independently of each other, much like a chameleon. Male seahorses, rather than the female, become pregnant and give birth. The female deposits her eggs into the male's brood pouch where they are fertilized and incubated until they hatch. The young receive no parental care after birth. There are over 35 species of seahorses and are mainly found in shallow tropical and temperate waters throughout the world.

Snowflake moray eel
Echidna nebulosa

The snowflake moray eel has a white body with small black spots. Look closely – the best time to view these animals here is early morning or late afternoon. Snowflake moray eels are found from Hawaii southward to Australia, westward through the islands of the Indo-Pacific to the East Indies, and across the Indian Ocean to the coast of Africa. They are also found in the eastern Central Pacific from southern Baja California, Mexico, and from Costa Rica to northern Colombia. They live between rocks and corals of intertidal reef flats, also in shallow lagoon and seaward reefs to depths of between 2 and 30 metres. They feed mainly on crustaceans.

toronto ZOO

Yabby

Yabbies are Australian crayfish with approximately 100 species. This is the second highest diversity of crayfish in the world behind North America. Yabbies live in a variety of habitats from lakes and streams to burrows in seasonally flooded areas.

Komodo Dragon
Varanus komodoensis

Male Komodos can measure up to 3 m long and weigh more than 130 kg (287 lbs). Females are generally half the size of males. The first two dragons to hatch at the Toronto Zoo averaged 140 g and 46 cm in length. During their first year, young Komodos spend most of their time in trees (where they are safer from predation) feeding on insects and geckos. After a year when they are approximately 1.3 m in length, the dragons will start foraging on the ground for snakes, birds, pigs, goats, and deer. The large dragons may consume up to 80 percent of their own body weight in one meal. Researchers have discovered specialized glands along the jaw that secrete chemicals that inhibit blood clotting and lower the blood pressure of prey. Their saliva also contains high concentrations of bacteria that causes severe infections in animals they attack. Komodo dragons are severely endangered in their natural habitat. It is estimated that there are as few as 5,000 Komodo dragons left in the wild.

> Found on four small islands in Indonesia, including Komodo Island, the Komodo dragon is the largest lizard in the world.

White-lipped Python
Liasis albertisii

White-lipped pythons do have white lips; however, the rest of their body is spectacularly iridescent in colour ranging from coppery-brown to black. These small- to medium-size terrestrial snakes live in the tropical forests of northern Australia. Pythons are ambush predators, which means they sit and wait for their prey and attack at just the right moment when success is probable. The white-lipped python is one of the quickest and most powerful constricting snakes. Their prey includes small mammals and nesting birds.

Green Tree Python
Morelia viridis

Found in New Guinea and northeastern Australia, the green tree python is well adapted to spend most of its time up in trees. Their bright green colouring provides good camouflage among the tropical leaves. Their tail is strongly prehensile for grasping onto branches; they also wiggle their tails to lure birds closer. Green tree pythons have enlarged teeth that assist in catching and holding prey (small mammals and birds). Young pythons differ in colour from adults — they can be orange, bright yellow, or red.

Emerald Tree Boa
Corallus caninus

The green tree python is almost indistinguishable from the emerald tree boa, which is found on the other side of the Pacific Ocean in tropical South America. Their colouring, resting postures (looped over tree branches), enlarged front teeth, and prehensile tail are all characteristics common to both snakes. This is an example of how two animals that are not closely related, adapted to look and act alike because they evolved in the same ecological conditions. These two snakes differ reproductively however; the emerald tree boa gives birth to live young and the green tree python lays eggs.

Like all snakes, the green tree python and emerald tree boa swallow their prey whole which is digested by strong acids in their stomach.

AUSTRALASIA

toronto **ZOO**

Macleay's Spectre
Extatosoma tiaratum

This insect resembles dried leaves and is easily camouflaged among foliage. Sometimes called spiny stick insects, Macleay's spectres have tiny spines on their head, body, and legs with leaf-like appendages extending from their legs and abdomen. Their colour ranges from brown to red to green. Males may grow up to 9 cm long, with a slender, elongated body. Females are usually 12–14 cm in length and stouter than males. Also, males have a set of fully functional wings, whereas females have wings but are incapable of flying. Females can lay eggs without being fertilized. These unfertile eggs hatch two years later and are always female.

In many species of stick insects, the females are considerably bigger than males.

Central Bearded Dragon
Acanthodraco vitticeps

Central bearded dragons have become accustomed to living in the harsh conditions of Australia's interior. They inhabit open woodlands, arid scrub, and deserts, where they bask in the sun. As omnivores, bearded dragons eat a variety of plant and animal materials such as insects, small animals, and, occasionally, fruit, leaves and flowers. However, during seasons when food is not as readily available, they can survive on nutrients and fat reserves stored in their large abdomen. If necessary, they will even burrow into the ground and remain dormant for long periods of time until the unfavourable weather conditions, such as extreme heat or cold, improve. These beautiful dragons possess a flared-out throat that looks like a beard, giving them their name.

Juveniles and female central bearded dragons, also called inland bearded dragons, will "wave" at aggressive older males when confronted.

toronto ZOO

Marine Toad
Bufo marinus

Marine toads were originally found only in parts of Central and South America. However, they were introduced to Australia and many other countries to control grey-back beetles that were pests to sugar cane crops. The toads eventually spread beyond the fields and down the east coast of Australia. Their numbers increased quickly and soon their diet included many species other than the beetles. Marine toads have glands on both sides of their head that contain a poison lethal to animals as large as dogs and cats. Unfortunately, species native to Australia (and other regions where these toads have been introduced) generally suffer if they feed on these unfamiliar amphibians. Despite the impact they have on the ecological balance of the region, marine toads are a delight to children and others who discover them.

> Marine toads are one of the largest species of toads.

Southern Hairy-nosed Wombat
Lasiorhinus latrifrons

Wombats are shy, nocturnal animals that live in burrows or warrens, about 3 m underground. Warrens can be up to 100 m long (the length of a football field!) and have up to 23 entrances. Temperature underground remains constant at 21°C. They are the world's largest burrowing marsupial, as long as 1.2 m, with a short tail. They feed on grasses, bark, and roots. Adapted to a desert climate, wombats do not sweat or drink from a water source; they take in moisture from the plants they eat. Females are sexually mature at three years of age and bear only one offspring a year. Gestation is slightly less than two weeks, and pouch life is 6–7 months before they are weaned at 8–9 months.

> The wombat's pouch faces backwards to avoid being filled with dirt while digging. Also, would you have guessed? The wombat's nearest relative is the koala!

toronto ZOO

Tawny Frogmouth
Podargus strigoides

The frogmouth is a nocturnal hunter with silent flight. Its toes are adapted for perching. It captures its food on the ground, pouncing on insects, scorpions, frogs, small birds, or mice. Resting motionless during the day, it appears to be sleeping; however, its upper eyelids are only lowered halfway so the bird is still alert and watching. Frogmouths resemble owls but they are actually related to whippoorwills and night hawks.

The plumage of males and females is the same. The only way to distinguish them is by the iris of the eyes: the female's eyes are large and round with a yellow iris and black pupil, and the male has a ring of orange-brown surrounding the iris.

Frilled Lizard
Chlamydosaurus kingii

The frilled lizard is found across northern Australia and southern New Guinea. It lives in the forest canopy of sub-humid to semi-arid grassy woodlands and dry forests, coming down from the trees to search for food which consists mostly of invertebrates, but also small mammals. The frilled lizard's most distinctive feature is the ruff or frill around its neck which lies over the shoulder until erected. This frill is a thin fold of skin surrounding the throat, which when extended may measure 30 cm across. The frill is supported by a set of cartilaginous rods connected to the muscles of the tongue and jaws. When alarmed, the mouth opens wide and the frill is extended around the head. They frequently run on two feet and can hiss when alarmed.

Short-beaked Echidna
Tachyglossus aculeatus

Echidnas are covered in sharp, hollow spines (up to 60 cm long). Their snouts stick out and are used to help catch prey. The echidna breaks into termite or ant nests using its snout and sharp claws and catches the insects inside with its long, sticky tongue. Along with the platypus, echidnas are the only egg-laying mammals (called

monotremes). Echidnas incubate a rubbery-skinned egg in a small backward facing pouch for ten days before it hatches. As echidnas lack nipples, the mammary glands secrete milk through patches on the skin from which the young lick up milk. The young are cast out of the pouch when their spines start to form.

In cold weather or when food is scarce, echidnas go into a state of hibernation. They have been known to go without food and water for 117 days.

Brush-tailed Bettong
Bettongia penicillata

The name bettong comes from the Aboriginal word for "small kangaroo." Another nocturnal marsupial found in Australia, the brush-tailed bettong once inhabited more than 60 percent of the country but is now only found in less than 1 percent. Many factors have led to its demise, including natural predation and habitat destruction. Unlike kangaroos and wallabies, their tail is not used for balance; they move about bipedally and rarely use their forefeet.

When gathering materials for its nest, a bettong picks up grass and twigs with its front limbs, pushes the material towards its back feet and then to its tail. The tail is used to carry the material to its nest.

AUSTRALASIA

toronto ZOO

Sugar Glider
Petaurus breviceps

Sugar gliders use their flying membranes to glide through the trees of Australian rainforests. The flying membrane is a piece of loose skin that extends from the wrist to the ankle. Their long, furry tail helps the gliders balance when they are soaring. Gliders sleep and rest in trees, making leaf nests in hollows or holes of trees, such as the eucalyptus. They feed on blossom nectar, sap from the branches (which they extract using their powerful incisors), insects, larvae, and small vertebrates. When gliders feed among the blossoms, pollen sticks to their fur and whiskers. The pollen is transferred to blossoms on other trees, resulting in cross-pollination.

 The longest recorded flight of a sugar glider is a distance of 45.6 m!

Black-faced Kangaroo
Macropus fuliginosus melanops

As one of many marsupials from Australia, the black-faced kangaroo female is ready to breed at two years and the male is ready six months later. The female produces a single, underdeveloped offspring that is both blind and hairless and about the size of a lima bean. The newborn claws its way up the front of its mother to the pouch where it clamps firmly onto a teat. Led by its sense of smell it will die if it loses its way. The trip is about 15 cm long and takes about three minutes. The joey leaves the pouch at about six months old for short periods but returns for rest and food up to 18 months of age.

 There are 56 species of kangaroos and wallabies that range in size from 0.5 kg to 90 kg. Their life span is generally seven years but can sometimes reach 20 years. Kangaroos belong to the Family Macropodidae, which literally means "big feet."

Emu
Dromaius novaehollandiae

This large bird, found only in Australia, is mainly brownish-grey except for the sides of the head and neck, which are naked and bright blue in colour. The emu grows up to 1.5–1.8 m and weighs approximately 55 kg. Emus breed at two years old. The male incubates the eggs without the hen and will seldom leave the nest during this time. If he does, he may cover the eggs with leaves and trampled vegetation making the dark green eggs very hard to see. After 58–61 days, the eggs hatch and both parents take part in raising the young.

The emu is the world's second-largest bird – the ostrich is the largest.

Bennett's Wallaby
Macropus rufogriseus

Bennett's wallaby, also known as red-necked wallaby, is found in southeastern Australia and Tasmania. They prefer coastal brushy areas or open forests where they can feed on leafy shrubs and grass. Wallabies have many characteristics similar to kangaroos; however, they are smaller in size. Their strong, long hind limbs (much stronger than the forelimbs) allow them to run fast, escaping from danger. Their fur is grey with red around the neck and shoulders. They also have a long, thick tail, which aids their balance. Young wallabies and kangaroos are called "joeys." Joeys can ride in their mother's pouch until 8-11 months of age.

Like other marsupials, wallabies lick their hands and forearms excessively when they are nervous, excited, or sweating in order to release body heat.

AUSTRALASIA

toronto ZOO

Eurasia

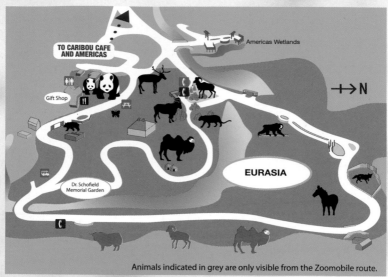

TO CARIBOU CAFE AND AMERICAS

Americas Wetlands

Gift Shop

EURASIA

Dr. Schofield Memorial Garden

N

Animals indicated in grey are only visible from the Zoomobile route.

*T*his vast region ranges from highly populated cities to untouched wild expanses. From chains of mountains, lakes, sea coasts, volcanoes, forests, and plains, Europe has many geographic landscapes. Asia encompasses deserts, vast plains called "steppes," high plateaus, the Himalayan mountains, coastal areas, and islands. Both range from extreme cold to warm coastal climates. Explore the outdoor exhibits of Eurasia at the Zoo, while enjoying a walk along the Zoo's waterway. Here you will encounter animals such as: the impressive Stellar's sea eagle – a relic of the ice age, red pandas, camels, reindeer, Przewalski's horses, and snow leopards.

Red Panda
Ailurus fulgens refulgens

An endangered species, the red panda's diet consists primarily of bamboo but also other plants and roots. Similar to giant pandas, red pandas have a bony thumb-like structure on each forepaw that helps them grasp bamboo. It is covered in red fur with a ringed tail and distinctive white markings on its face. The red colouring allows the red panda to blend in with reddish moss and white lichen in fir trees. Red pandas are born blind and stay that way for 21–30 days, thus remaining dependent on their mother for some time. To produce enough milk for her cubs, the mother will eat three times the normal quantity of bamboo.

Red pandas are most closely related to raccoons but are so unique that scientists have classified them into a family of their own.

Bactrian Camel
Camelus bactrianus

What's in a camel's humps? The humps store fat that nourish the animal when the food supply is scarce. Camels can store about 36 kg of fat in their humps, and as they use up the fat, the humps get smaller. Their skin does not contain sweat glands; therefore, they lose moisture from their bodies very slowly. Moisture is obtained by drinking water and eating desert plants. In winter, plants provide enough moisture for camels to go without drinking water for several weeks — which makes their treks across the desert manageable.

EURASIA

toronto ZOO

Przewalski's Horse
Equus caballus przewalskii

The Przewalski's horse is now extinct in the wild, but it used to inhabit the vast grasslands of central Asia. The Przewalski's horses living in captivity today descended from just ten animals originally brought from Europe. Colonel Nikolai Przewalski discovered these horses that are now named after him. Przewalski's horses can survive on desert scrub that a domestic horse would reject. Herds range in size from 3–20 and are led by a stallion that will defend his mares against any danger that approaches. Stallions will fight to have this leadership, engaging in a battle that may last hours until the weaker horse succumbs to exhaustion.

 Through conservation efforts of zoos all around the world, the number of horses in captivity has significantly increased since 1960, making this one of the most successful international efforts to rescue a species threatened with extinction. These captive efforts have made it possible to reintroduce animals back into their historic range.

Steller's Sea Eagle
Haliaeetus pelagicus

The Steller's sea eagle is one of the most impressive birds in the world. Considered relics of the Ice Age, they are the heaviest bird of prey and more than double the weight of a bald eagle. Females can weigh as much as 9 kg (20 lbs) and have a wing span of 2.5 metres (8 feet). They are predominantly dark brown to black with a large white wing patch and white rump, legs and tail. They have a large orange to yellow bill. They are a coastal bird found along the Bering Strait in Russia. Occasionally one can be seen in the Aleutian Islands of Alaska. They nest in trees

or rock faces and are mainly non-migratory. In the wild they feed mainly on fish, waterfowl and carrion. The average bird would eat about 300 grams (two medium rats) a day.

Eurasian Eagle Owl
Bubo bubo

This is one of the two heaviest and longest-winged owls. Males can weigh as much as 2.8 kg and females 4.2 kg with a wing span of 1.6 – 1.8 metres. Eurasian eagle owls range across southern France, Italy, Germany, Czech Republic, Austria, Iraq, Iran, Tibet, China, and Hong Kong. The owls prey on a variety of small mammals, such as rodents, rabbits, hedgehogs and shrews. Larger mammals such as fox, marmot and small deer are also hunted. Though it does hunt in flight, the Eurasian eagle owl usually uses a perch. It's eyes are 2.2 times larger than birds of similar weight, and as a nocturnal hunter, its night vision is ten times more acute than that of humans. Once fixed on its prey, a silent approach is achieved by adaptations to the flight feathers to reduce turbulence and sound. Life span is 20 years.

Domestic Yak
Bos mutus grunniens

Yaks are found throughout the Himalayan region of south central Asia, the Tibetan Plateau, and as far north as Mongolia. They eat herbs, leaves, grasses, and lichens. They drink frequently during the summer and will eat snow in winter. Domesticated yaks are much smaller than wild yaks, and vary much more in colour, from black to light yellow-brown, with some having mottled white patches on their sides and backs. Both wild and domesticated yaks have long shaggy hair to insulate them from the cold. Both males and females have horns. Bulls fight for the possession of the females by pushing against each other with their foreheads, but rarely do damage. Domestic yaks require very little food and can withstand very cold temperatures of -40°C. During severe blizzards, they turn their broad bushy tails into the storm and remain motionless for hours. Yaks are one of the most important domesticated beasts in Tibet. They provide transportation, meat, milk, and their dried dung is used as fuel. Yaks are unable to moo and instead grunt. Their scientific name translates from Latin to: Bos: an ox and Grunnio (grunniens): I grunt.

toronto ZOO

EURASIA

Snow Leopard
Uncia uncia

This leopard lives primarily in the Himalayan Mountains in rocky areas, snow fields, glaciers, and alpine meadows. The snow leopard is highly adapted to living in cold mountain temperatures; for example, its long, thick tail acts as a scarf in cold weather when it's curled around the face and body. Also, thick fur pads on the back legs above the ankle protect against cold and ice. Their small rounded ears and head reduce heat loss, and they have a well-developed chest and enlarged nasal cavity that help them breathe in the cold, thin high-altitude air. The snow leopard can leap as far as 15 m, allowing it to surprise its prey. They feed mainly on mountain goats, deer, and sheep, as well as other small mammals. Snow leopards generally live about 15 years in the wild. They are solitary creatures, except during breeding season. Unfortunately, they are now endangered. Extensive conservation efforts are trying to save this species.

The snow leopard's thick tail is about 1 m long, almost the same length as the leopard's body.

EXHIBIT PLANTS

Various factors must be determined before plants are selected for exhibits, such as:

- What are the animal's habits? Does it dig? Will it use the plants to climb out of the exhibit? Will it eat the plants?
- Are the plants non-toxic?
- Will the plants obstruct the visitors' view?
- Are the plants arranged biogeographically (according to the region of the world where they would naturally be found)?
- As a recreational feature, will the plant support the animal's weight?
- What is the environment like? Is it really hot, wet, or dry? How much light is available?

Australasia and Eurasia Plants

Gum Tree
Eucalyptus species, Myrtle Family, Myrtaceae

Eucalyptus, or gum trees, dominate forested areas of the Australian landscape. These tall trees have trunks with characteristic patchy, shedding bark. The juvenile leaves are quite different from mature foliage. In general, young leaves are broader, more blunt, and paler in colour. At the Zoo, eucalyptus trees grow rapidly, therefore they must be cut back regularly to keep them from growing through the pavilion roof. Eucalyptus can grow up to 114 m tall with seedlings potentially growing 1.5 m in one season. Eucalyptus plants produce oils that are used as stimulants, antiseptics, and aromatics. Eucalyptus oil is a common ingredient in cough drops and other cold remedies. Eucalyptus is an important plant to the wildlife of Australia: koalas eat the leaves of this plant; kangaroos find shade under it; and fruit bats sip nectar from its flowers.

Bamboo
Grass Family, Poaceae

Bamboo is the world's fastest-growing plant. It is also one of the earth's most primitive grasses, existing 100–200 million years before humans. There are 1,200–1,500 species of bamboo found in many countries throughout the world. The plants range in size from only a few centimetres to 40 m tall. Bamboo has an immense number of uses. It is used for construction and weaving because of its amazing strength. Bamboo is used to build scaffolding for the construction of skyscrapers in Japan. Giant pandas and red pandas feed almost exclusively on bamboo leaves and stems.

toronto ZOO

Index of Animals

🦓 toronto **ZOO**

Index of Plants and Trees